THREE GENERATIONS OF COOKING

with

the *DOCTOR,* the *DIETITIAN,* and the *DIVA*

Plant-based Wellness Cookbook

JAMI DULANEY, MD
ADDIE MAJNARIC, RDN
ALFREDA DULANEY

A family with love for cooking and helping others reach optimal health and wellness through plant based nutrition – that is what the Dulaney ladies are all about! Step into the kitchen with three generations as they put a plant strong twist on tradition with these doctor and dietitian approved meals.

© Copyright 2019 Jaimela Dulaney and Addie Majnaric
Printed in the United States of America
All rights reserved

www.doctordulaney.com
ISBN: 978-1-7339677-0-9
Library of Congress
Book design by Jordan Aquila

First Edition: May 2019

TABLE OF CONTENTS

Chapter 9:
Desserts that Heal **151**

INTRODUCTION

Food has always been a topic of conversation in the Dulaney family.

My mother was a meal planner. She had to be. She worked two jobs, ran two households and was the matriarch of the family. We joke that she and my father did not cross-train. She was in charge of all things house-related. She cooked every night after working as a bookkeeper, so she needed to have those menus in mind when she did the majority of the grocery shopping once a week.

Because of our busy schedules, we feel that planning our meals and shopping once a week makes eating nutritiously at home more convenient.

When we first became plant-based, menu planning became even more important, given the need to alter our old standard dishes, and add new plant-based recipes.

Sometimes it was as simple as converting a traditional meal into a plant-based meal by eliminating meat and adding beans. Other times, it was a totally new recipe to try.

Nevertheless, it has been helpful to jot down a menu plan for three days at a time. We developed go-to meals that everyone liked and that we enjoyed preparing. We saved the more complicated recipes for the weekends when we had more time. As we became more versed in plant-strong meals, we could look in the refrigerator and plan a menu with what was on hand.

Nothing replaces a home-cooked meal. You have control over the source and the type of ingredients. You know the hygiene of the kitchen. Your home is a safe environment that allows the family to talk freely and catch up on the day. Involving your family in meal preparation and cleanup provides valuable time together and valuable teaching moments.

There are studies showing that when families eat dinner together, children do better in school and are less likely to have behavioral problems. You will also save time and certainly money by eating unprocessed and at home. Many people with health problems in our practice describe growing up on take-out and processed foods. Salt and oil are additives to make poor-quality food taste the same. As a result, people develop a taste for salt and oil and have no idea what the actual vegetables truly taste like.

There is a disconnect between food and health in our world today. Then again, if the food you consume is all brown and tastes the same, why would it matter what you eat?

This book is designed to share our favorite meals. They are easy to get on the table while also nutritious and delicious. They are colorful, nutrient-dense, and also familiar.

We have used many of these recipes in our nutrition class to demonstrate cooking preparation and techniques. They also served as a demonstration of the plant-strong nutrients we would like to eat each day. The meals are appropriate for everyone, and I encourage you to feed your children the same food you eat — not "kid food" — as soon as they begin eating solids. With blenders and food processors, there is no need to buy jarred baby food of unknown quality. Children will transition to your cooking if they have experienced these tastes from early childhood.

We are grateful for the opportunity to share cooking tips, techniques and meals from three generations of Dulaney women. We wish each of you the same joy we have experienced in cooking and eating together as a family.

DEDICATION

To Grandma Addie and her Salt Risen Bread

My grandmother Addie Dulaney was a wonderful person and cook whose life was shortened by diabetes and coronary artery disease.

I became a physician to help prolong the lives of others by treating and helping them prevent these lifestyle diseases through a whole-food, plant-based diet and exercise.

I grew up watching Grandma Addie make this Salt Risen Bread. It is a process that takes many hours to complete, and requires careful attention. In fact, it was such an art, that a bakery was opened up many years after her passing featuring this special bread.

I have altered her recipe to remove the oil and substitute soy milk for dairy. Because cake yeast or dry active yeast was not readily available in a lot of farming communities, this bread uses the fermentation broth of potatoes instead, which gives it a heavy, dense texture. I used white bread flour to keep the recipe as authentic as possible.

While this recipe does take a little time and patience, we are excited to share this special Irish treat with you. We hope you enjoy it as much as our family does.

Ingredients

3 medium potatoes
2 tablespoons cornmeal
Pinch of baking soda
4 tablespoons unrefined sugar
1 quart soy milk
5 pounds bread flour
1 teaspoon salt

Directions

1. Slice potatoes thin and place them in a quart jar.
2. Add 2 tablespoons cornmeal.
3. Add baking soda.
4. Add 2 tablespoons sugar
5. Pour in 2 cups boiling water.
6. Cover jar loosely and let it sit in a warm place until morning. (I use my oven, keeping the door propped open with a dishtowel to keep the temperature from 90-100°F.) By morning, you should see 1 inch of foam and smell fermentation.
7. Scald one quart of plain soy milk. Remove from heat when you start to see tiny bubbles form around the edge of the saucepan. Boiling will destroy the yeast in your starter.
8. Add 1 tablespoon sugar.
9. In a mixing bowl, add 1-1/2 cups of liquid from the jar, plus the scalded milk and sugar.
10. Add enough flour to make a batter. Cover and set the bowl in a warm place and let rise for a few hours or until doubled in size.
11. Add one teaspoon salt.
12. Add one tablespoon sugar.
13. Add flour until soft dough forms.
14. Knead for 20 minutes.
15. Let rise 3 hours.
16. Bake at 350°F for 40-50 minutes or until the top is golden brown.

Yield: 5-6 loaves.

PER SERVING: Calories = 135; Total fat = 0.2g; Total carbohydrates = 27g; Protein = 5g; Sodium = 8mg ; Fiber = 1.2g

Chapter 1:

Breakfast Ideas to Start Your Day Strong

Oil-Free Granola

Many people think of granola as a crunchy health food, when, in fact, most commercial brands contain multiple oils and sugars, making store-bought granola a high-calorie, high-fat and high-sugar breakfast.

Our nutrition students tell us they want a crunch at breakfast, and that's why they turn to granola. This recipe is a healthy alternative that provides crunch — and nutrients — without oil or simple sugars.

Once you have made this basic version, try adding pumpkin pie spice or frozen cherries to the apple in the mixture. The possibilities are endless.

I use a dehydrator, but you can also bake the granola at the lowest oven setting until you get the desired crunch.

Store your granola in a mason jar, and add it to your fruit bowl in the morning or as a healthy snack with fruit instead of an energy bar.

Walnuts are a great source of omega-3 fatty acids, and sunflower and pumpkin seeds are a great source of magnesium and iron. But nuts and seeds are high calorie-dense foods. This is why I would limit granola to a condiment with fruit as opposed to a bowl of granola topped with fruit.

Ingredients

2 medium apples
1/2 cup walnuts
1/2 cup sunflower seeds
1/2 cup pumpkin seeds
1/2 cup raisins
1 cup old-fashioned oats
1 teaspoon cinnamon
1 teaspoon ginger
1/4 teaspoon ground cloves

Directions

1. Soak walnuts, sunflower seeds and pumpkin seeds for at least 4 hours in water. I use a mason jar and leave it on the counter overnight.
2. Chop apples coarsely and place in a food processor. Using the S blade, blend until moderately smooth. Transfer the contents to a large mixing bowl. (No need to wash the food processor before the next step.)
3. Drain sunflower seeds, pumpkin seeds, and walnuts and add to the food processor. Blend until fairly smooth and transfer to the same large mixing bowl.
4. Add raisins, oats and spices and mix thoroughly.
5. Spread on a parchment-lined cookie sheet or a non-stick dehydrator tray until about 1/4-inch thick.
6. Dehydrate for 24 hours at 115°F. At 12 hours in the dehydrator, flip using a second non-stick sheet and tray. Alternatively, bake in the oven at 180-200°F until crunchy.
7. Break apart granola and store in a mason jar. Eat within two weeks to maintain freshness — but it will not last that long!

SERVINGS: 12

PER SERVING: Calories = 210; Total fat = 11g; Total carbohydrates = 27g; Protein = 9g; Sodium = 3mg; Fiber = 5g; Iron = 12%

Oil-Free Granola

Teff Pancakes

Teff is an ancient grain packed with nutrients. A quarter-cup provides 5 grams of protein, 15% of the recommended daily allowance (RDA) for iron, 6% of the RDA for calcium, and 5 grams of fiber. It is also a gluten-free way to make pancakes.

By adding 2 tablespoons of cacao powder to the mix, you can bump up the antioxidants and get a hint of chocolate. We find these pancakes are great before a long bike ride or after a long run. They also warm up nicely in the toaster oven, so make a few extra on the weekend for your family to enjoy during the week.

Ingredients

- ¾ cup teff flour
- 1/2 cup cornmeal, not flour
- 2 tablespoons cacao powder
- 2 teaspoons baking powder
- 1 mashed banana
- 1-1/4 cups soy milk
- 1/3 cup water
- 1 teaspoon vanilla
- 2 tablespoons maple syrup
- 2 teaspoons grated lemon zest

Directions

1. Combine dry ingredients and whisk thoroughly.
2. Add mashed banana and liquid ingredients. Texture should be a thickened batter that pours easily.
3. Add water gradually if needed. I make a double batch for 3-4 people and serve with a fruit bowl.
4. We also use whole fruit spread or jam without added sugar. Here are a few quick and easy alternatives:

Raspberry: Blend a cup of fresh or frozen raspberries (or berries of your choice), 1/4 cup of nut milk and a ripe banana with an immersion blender.

Chocolate sauce: Blend 1 banana, 3 tablespoons cacao powder, and 1/4 cup nut milk.

For extra sweetness, you can blend a date into the above. Soaking the dates helps make them blend better and you can use some of the water for extra flavor.

SERVINGS: 8

PER SERVING: Calories = 116; Total fat = 1g; Total carbohydrates = 25g; Protein = 4g; Sodium = 29mg; Fiber = 4g; Iron = 10%

Teff Pancakes

Teff Porridge

This is a great alternative to oatmeal. It makes me think of my childhood days of CoCo Wheats — but this is a whole-grain, healthy version.

The spices make this dish. I even add a secret heaping teaspoon of matcha green tea powder and a tablespoon of cacao powder as the porridge is cooking for an additional source of antioxidants. (Matcha tea is the whole leaf powdered, so all the antioxidants are retained from the tea leaf.)

This porridge takes a little longer to cook than oatmeal, so I usually make this on the weekend. It will keep in the refrigerator for a couple of days and can be heated easily in the microwave. I serve this with a fruit bowl on the side, but a sliced banana and blueberries are a great topping as well.

Ingredients

1 cup teff
3 cups water
4 dates
1/4 cup raisins
1 teaspoon ginger
1/2 teaspoon cinnamon
1/4 teaspoon nutmeg
1 teaspoon matcha green tea powder
1 tablespoon cacao powder
1/4 cup chopped walnuts

Directions

1. Cook teff in a medium-sized saucepan on high heat. Allow the grains to pop.
2. Add water and bring to a boil, then reduce to simmer.
3. Add spices, raisins, dates and walnuts and allow the porridge to simmer until it thickens, about 15 minutes.
4. Top with bananas or blueberries, if desired, and serve.

SERVINGS: 4

PER SERVING: Calories = 389; Total fat = 7g; Total carbohydrates = 79g; Protein = 9g; Sodium = 11mg; Fiber = 10g; Iron = 28%

Teff Porridge

Addie's Blender Waffles

I typically save waffles and pancakes for the weekends because they usually take a little longer to make and don't hold me as long because of the flours used. These waffles are a different story. Quick to make, easy to clean up (you only dirty a blender and your waffle iron) and packed with fiber. Think of these waffles as a fun way to serve your usual oatmeal!

You can add more fruit to your blender or serve it on the side. Blueberries make these waffles a fun blue color and cherries or strawberries give you a bright pink breakfast option. To make pancakes from this recipe, simply thin out the batter with water or your choice of plant milk.

With a press of your blender's button, you will quickly have a two-serving midweek breakfast treat.

Ingredients

- 1 cup oats
- 2 tablespoons ground flaxseed
- 1/2 teaspoon baking powder
- 1/2 teaspoon cinnamon
- 1 cup water
- 1 banana
- 1 teaspoon vanilla extract

Directions

1. Place oats in a blender and blend to a flour-like consistency.
2. Add ground flaxseed, baking powder and cinnamon and blend again.
3. Preheat waffle iron.
4. Add banana, water and vanilla to dry mix, blending until a smooth batter has formed.
5. To extend or thin the batter, add an additional 1/4 cup water.
6. Scoop batter onto the hot waffle iron and cook according to your iron's directions.

SERVINGS: 2

PER SERVING: Calories = 422; Total fat = 9g; Total carbohydrates = 74g; Protein = 15g; Sodium = 24mg; Fiber = 16g; Iron = 25%

Addie's Blender Waffles

Quinoa Fruit Bowl

While oatmeal is a wonderful choice for your first meal of the day, this quinoa fruit bowl provides an option to add variety to your nutritional regimen. Variety in your food helps keep things interesting and exposes you to assorted nutrients.

Each spoonful of this dish contains a hearty dose of fiber, plant-based protein, antioxidants and omega-3 fatty acids.

You'll stay full and maintain energy for all your morning tasks with this breakfast option.

Ingredients

1 cup cooked quinoa (1 cup dry plus 2 cups water)
1-2 cups berries of your choice
1 sliced banana
1/4 cup walnuts
1/4 teaspoon cinnamon
Optional: Add dried berries of your choice

Directions

1. Place dry quinoa and water in a medium saucepan.
2. Bring to a boil and reduce heat to simmer until quinoa grains have popped, and the water has been absorbed (about 5-7 minutes).
3. Quinoa can be served warm or cold.
4. Combine all ingredients in a bowl and enjoy!

SERVINGS: 1

PER SERVING: Calories = 527; Total fat = 23g; Total carbohydrates = 79g; Protein = 12g; Sodium = 11mg; Fiber = 16g; Iron = 18%

Quinoa Fruit Bowl

Pumpkin Spice Pancakes

It's a cool fall weekend. The leaves are changing, pumpkin patches are everywhere, and you are cozying up on a lazy Saturday.

What would be the cherry on top? These pumpkin spice pancakes, of course! Super moist, full of autumn flavor, and packed with fiber and vitamin A. Top with a sprinkle of pumpkin seeds, pair with in-season fruit, and your day is bound to be nothing less than wonderful.

Ingredients

2 cups flour (whole wheat or 1:1 gluten-free blends work)
2 teaspoons baking powder
2 teaspoons cinnamon
1 teaspoon ground ginger
1/2 teaspoon nutmeg
1/4 teaspoon ground clove
1-1/2 cups almond milk plus 2 tablespoons apple cider vinegar
1 cup pumpkin puree
2 teaspoons vanilla extract
1 tablespoon maple syrup OR molasses
1/2 cup water
Toppings: pecans, pumpkin seeds and/or maple syrup

Directions

1. Combine almond milk and vinegar in a medium-sized mixing bowl and set aside to curdle.
2. Combine all dry ingredients in a large mixing bowl.
3. Add all other wet ingredients to almond milk mixture.
4. Pour wet ingredients into dry ingredients, blending well.
5. Heat a nonstick griddle/pan on medium high heat.
6. Once pan is hot, pour about   cup batter into the pan.
7. Pancakes are ready to flip when bubbles begin to form.

SERVINGS: 6

PER SERVING: Calories = 179; Total fat = 2g; Total carbohydrates = 37g; Protein = 6g; Sodium = 75mg; Fiber = 6g; Iron = 11%

Pumpkin Spice Pancakes

Tofu No-Egg Sandwich

During marathon training, I do my long runs on Saturday mornings. I usually eat dates and a few sweet energy gels during the run. After the run, I am ready for some "real" food, and am also tired of sweet things.

This sandwich is a great quick and savory brunch, and a great recovery meal after a strenuous workout. Adding just a pinch of black salt to the tofu gives the smell of an egg.

Tofu is a great protein source after a workout. Those worried about eating GMO soy should not eat animal products because animals, including farm-raised fish, are the largest consumers of this product. Tofu is made by coagulating non-GMO soy milk, similar to how cottage cheese is made. It is then pressed into blocks and pasteurized, increasing the shelf life to about 30 days. Soy contains phytoestrogens, which are estrogen receptor blockers. By blocking the receptor, there is a decrease in risk of estrogen promoting tumors such as breast cancer.

The extra tofu slices keep well in the refrigerator for a few days. Adding a bowl of fruit or a hydrating fruit smoothie to this recipe makes for a great post-workout meal.

Ingredients

- 1 box (14-ounce) extra-firm tofu
- 1 tablespoon light soy sauce
- 2 tablespoons water
- 1 tablespoon Dijon mustard
- 1 teaspoon cumin
- 2 teaspoons turmeric
- Pinch of black salt

Directions

1. Remove tofu from package, drain and rinse.
2. Slice tofu into 4 thin slices. Place on paper towels, cover with another towel, and place a heavier object on top to press out excess water. This will help to create a crispy tofu when cooking.
3. While tofu is being pressed, mix light soy sauce, water and mustard in a separate bowl.
4. Marinate tofu in the mixture, either by placing in the previous bowl or by coating it on a separate pan.
5. Heat a non-stick skillet. Sprinkle turmeric and cumin to coat one side of each slice of tofu, then add a pinch or two of black salt. Place the seasoned side down on the skillet.
6. While the slices are heating, repeat the seasoning on the other side.
7. Flip each slice to cook both sides; you may want to flip a few times.
8. These cooked tofu slices can be placed on sprouted grain, oil-free bread for a sandwich or on a large, mixed-greens salad with avocado and tomatoes for a delicious breakfast/lunch treat.

SERVINGS: 4

PER SERVING: Calories = 103; Total fat = 6g; Total carbohydrates = 5g; Protein = 10g; Sodium = 146mg; Fiber = 1g; Iron = 15%

Tofu No-Egg Sandwich

Tofu Scramble

A tofu scramble can be enjoyed any time of day, but it does serve well as a savory alternative to change up your breakfast routine! We have used this recipe many times as a "breakfast for dinner" option when a quick meal is needed. This recipe is completely balanced with colorful vegetables, greens, deliciously seasoned tofu and nutrient-dense potatoes. The tofu can easily be interchanged with chickpeas for the same nutritionally balanced meal.

Ingredients

1 box (14-ounce) firm tofu
3 medium golden potatoes
1 bunch kale
1 cup fresh salsa
2 tomatoes
1 cup sliced mushrooms
1/2 onion
2 teaspoons turmeric
1 tablespoon nutritional yeast
1 tablespoon garlic
1 teaspoon smoked paprika
1/4 teaspoon cumin
Pinch of black salt (optional)
Pepper to taste

Directions

1. Remove and rinse tofu; slice and dice, then set aside on a paper towel to let excess water drain.
2. Wash and peel potatoes, and dice into small chunks.
3. Add diced potatoes and a cup of water to a saucepan. Bring to a boil, then cover and cook until soft. Drain excess water.
4. Add tofu to potatoes in the saucepan. Mix diced tofu and potatoes with your cooking spoon/spatula. Add spices (omit black salt to reduce sodium). Mix well until spices are evenly spread throughout, and your "scramble" has a nice golden color.
5. Wash and chop kale, tomatoes, onion and mushrooms. In a skillet, sauté chopped onion in water until translucent. Add kale and tomatoes. Cook until tender.
6. Add cooked greens and scramble to your plate. Top with fresh salsa.

SERVINGS: 6

PER SERVING: Calories = 160, Total fat = 3.5g; Total carbohydrates = 26.3g; , Protein; 11.4g; Sodium = 52.5mg; Fiber = 4.8g

Tofu Scramble

Chia Seed Breakfast Parfait

People say there's no time to make breakfast, and then grab a processed bar or stop at a drive-through. I never hear people say there's no time to wander into the kitchen after dinner looking for a snack. That's the perfect time to prepare breakfast for the next morning.

If you are tired of overnight oatmeal, this is a great twist on breakfast that is loaded with omega-3 fatty acids. You can take it to go in the morning if you're in a hurry or enjoy it with extra fruit at home. If you travel for work, carry chia seeds in a jar so you can enjoy this in your hotel room.

You can add your own twist by selecting different fruit. Blueberries give it a special purple color and boost phytonutrients. Fruit provides an abundance of nutrients to choose from each morning so why get in a rut?

Ingredients
- 3 tablespoons chia seeds
- 1/4 cup soy or almond milk
- 1/2 teaspoon vanilla
- 1/2 cup blueberries
- 1/2 banana

Directions for overnight version
1. Place chia seeds in a jar and cover with soy milk.
2. Add berries, bananas and vanilla.
3. Stir to mix chia seed throughout the fruit.
4. Cover and place in the refrigerator.
5. Enjoy the next morning.

Directions for morning version
1. Place chia seeds in a bowl and cover with soy milk.
2. Stir to completely wet the seeds, then microwave 1-1/2 minutes.
3. Add fruit and vanilla, then mix well and enjoy.

SERVINGS: 1

PER SERVING: Calories = 310; Total fat = 10g; Total carbohydrates = 42g; Protein = 12g; Sodium = 25mg; Fiber = 19g; Iron = 22%

Chia Seed Breakfast Parfait

Chapter 2:

Naturally Nutritious Smoothies

NATURALLY NUTRITIOUS SMOOTHIES

I believe smoothies are desserts or recovery drinks, and can be good sources of calories and nutrients when you're not feeling well. They also serve those needing to gain some weight or add additional nutrients after a surgery or illness.

If used as a meal replacement, smoothies are calorie-dense. They are, however, a great source of hydration and antioxidants after extended exercise.

Smoothies can be a good way to introduce children to different vegetables and fruits, and a better option than nut milks or juices as a drink. Children can choose the ingredients and can guess what color smoothie they will make, and parents can hide greens with colored fruits.

By adding greens to smoothies, you are still affecting taste buds that can be changed over a relatively short period of time. Don't forget that children need to learn the process of chewing. Drinking liquids and eating soft foods fails to develop the relationship between chewing and becoming satisfied. The liquids and soft foods take up less space in the GI tract, therefore lessening and delaying the sensation of fullness.

When you are trying to boost your nitric oxide production with greens, you won't get all the benefits if the greens are blended. They need time to come in contact with the microbes in your mouth and the amylase in your saliva to form nitric oxide. You will still get some benefit if you blend them coarsely, as well as when they are absorbed from your small intestine.

Kale-Blueberry-Banana

This is a great morning smoothie after a workout. Again, blending kale will decrease the nitric oxide potential one gets through chewing, but the second boost still occurs when it hits the small intestine. This is a good smoothie to introduce children to fruit and greens. Start with blueberries and banana and just a small handful of kale. This will be a purple smoothie that kids love. Gradually add more kale to get in those greens. Adding a tablespoon of cacao powder will make this a brown "chocolate" smoothie that is packed with nutrients.

Cherry-Banana-Cacao

Keeping a bag or two of frozen fruit is a great way to make a quick dessert that the whole family loves. This is my dessert smoothie. After an evening workout, I find this very hydrating and satisfying. Cacao contains an antioxidant called epicatechin that promotes enzymes associated with muscle cell growth.

Cherries are packed with antioxidants and the cacao powder makes this smoothie tastes like a chocolate cherry shake, but without the fat and full of flavor. This takes the place for evening ice cream for me. Top this with cacao nibs for a little crunch and pretty presentation.

Mango-Banana-Pineapple

My favorite time of the year in Florida is mango season. There are more than 40 different varieties of mangoes, each with a different flavor and texture. They are loaded with beta carotene and vitamin C. We freeze our leftover mangoes to keep for the off-season, but you can also purchase them frozen.

Pineapple has a lot of anti-inflammatory phytonutrients as well. I buy a whole pineapple and use the core because it contains the highest amount of the anti-inflammatory and anti-cancer enzyme bromelain. Pineapple with kale also makes a beautiful, bright green smoothie, so add a little kale for some extra nutrients and nitric oxide release.

Spinach-Banana–Berry-Melon

Summer is also melon season. Melons are loaded with vitamin C and are very hydrating after a workout. If you purchase a watermelon and have more than you can use, think about using it in a smoothie. Fruit is one of the best ways to hydrate and recover from endurance training and a great way to quickly recover from a hot day working in the yard. I usually have a smoothie immediately after my long runs or long bike rides on the weekend.

Ginger-Turmeric-Lemon-Orange-Pineapple

One of the great benefits of a plant-strong way of life is the lower incidence of infections. However, because of environmental superbugs and antibiotic resistance, infection is still quite possible even for us plant-strong folks. A person eating nutrient-dense and plant strong can fight off the symptoms of an infection much more quickly.

If I feel a cold coming on, I whip up this anti-inflammatory smoothie with ginger and turmeric. Lemon peel carries additional enzymes such as salvestrol Q40, and limonene, which have anti-cancer cell properties, anti-bacterial and anti-fungal properties. Salvestrol belongs to the phytoalexins, which are produced by plants to protect against fungi, bacteria, viruses, insects and ultraviolet light. In humans, they induce apoptosis or killing of cancer cells following activation by CYP1B1 enzyme. Interestingly, the amount of salvestrol appears greater in fruit that is produced without the use of pesticides because these fruits have to protect themselves.

I use about an inch each of fresh ginger and turmeric. I store my turmeric in the freezer to preserve freshness. If you don't have fresh root, use at least a teaspoon of each dried ground powder. In this smoothie, I use about ⅓ of a lemon including the peel. I use a whole orange and a 1/2 cup of fresh pineapple. Cover the ingredients with water and blend until smooth.

Chapter 3:

Let's Talk Salad

I tell a story in my nutrition classes about patients reporting their menus from the previous night. When asked what they had for dinner, they almost always say, "A salad." That is vague and not usually accurate. They believe they are telling me what I want to hear and are hoping I will stop asking.

Most people think of a salad as a dietary punishment they must eat until they achieve their weight-loss goal. It is one of those health foods not considered attractive or filling in its usual form. It is certainly not regarded as comfort food. Some people even see a salad as a distraction until the real meal is served.

These observations could not be further from the truth.

A salad can be bursting with flavor and nutritionally dense. Adding fruit to the greens eliminates the need for high-fat dressings. Adding a grain or starch can make it calorie-dense enough for a satisfying meal.

Raw foods at breakfast and lunch are easily digestible and give a burst of energy and nutrients without weighing you down for the afternoon. Adding a salad to dinner gives another burst of nutrients and fiber without the caloric density. This addition ultimately helps with portion control and calorie management.

These are some favorite go-to salads for lunch and dinner sides:

Jicama-Mango-Carrot Salad

Jicama is a root vegetable native to Mexico and South America that also grows great in my home state of Florida. When ripe, it produces a purple flower and pods. The seeds are not edible, but can easily be planted.

Jicama has a light, crunchy flavor similar to water chestnuts that some raw food recipes use finely diced as rice. It's a low-calorie, nutrient-dense vegetable high in fiber and vitamin C.

This simple salad is sweet and tasty, plus loaded with antioxidants. Adding a little cayenne pepper gives it a nice kick. For those who don't like cilantro, substitute parsley to keep the nitric oxide benefits of the salad. This salad goes especially well with our burritos.

Ingredients

- 1 medium to large jicama
- 1 carrot
- 1 mango
- 3 tablespoons chopped fresh cilantro
- 2 tablespoons lime juice or the juice of 2 limes
- 1 teaspoon chili powder

Directions

1. Thinly slice or shred carrots and jicama.
2. Thinly slice mango.
3. Toss with lime juice and sprinkle with chili pepper.
4. Garnish with cilantro before serving.

SERVINGS: 4

PER SERVING: Calories = 129; Total fat = 1g; Total carbohydrates = 31g; Protein = 2g; Sodium = 35mg; Fiber = 10g; Iron = 8%

Jicama-Mango-Carrot Salad

Arugula-Grapefruit Salad

Arugula ranks top among greens as a source of nitric oxide. Adding fruit to a salad is a great way to avoid using a creamy dressing, and in this salad, the bite of the arugula and the citrus complement each other well.

Shaved fennel adds a unique licorice flavor in another layer of taste. Fennel is loaded with vitamins and minerals such as potassium, calcium, iron, magnesium, vitamin A and vitamin C, and also contains many phytonutrients such as quercitin and anethole.

These nutrients shut down the intercellular signaling of alpha tumor necrosis factor, or TNF, which provides anti-inflammatory and anti-cancer effects. Together, this is a salad packed with iron, fiber and vitamin C. Add some grapes for additional color and phytonutrients.

This salad plates nicely, and is great to serve guests who are expecting bland, vegan food. Substitute an orange if the grapefruit interferes with your blood pressure or cholesterol medications. If you continue to eat your nitric oxide-producing vegetables, you will be off those medications in no time!

Ingredients

1 box arugula, washed and drained
1 large grapefruit
1 avocado
1 bulb of fennel
1 lemon
Black pepper

Directions

1. Chop grapefruit into small pieces.
2. Slice avocado into small pieces.
3. Shave the white portion of the fennel bulb into small, thin slices.
4. Place ingredients above in a large salad bowl with arugula, then squeeze lemon and add the juice.
5. Add black pepper to taste.

SERVINGS: 4

PER SERVING: Calories = 110; Total fat = 5g; Total carbohydrates = 15g; Protein = 3g; Sodium = 46mg; Fiber = 6g; Iron = 7%

Arugula-Grapefruit Salad

Moroccan Salad

This salad can stand alone as a nutrient-dense powerhouse meal. The unique spices mixed with kale make this a favorite. It is also a hearty and filling salad, thanks to the sweet potato and sunflower seeds. Its nutrients include omega-3 fatty acids, beta carotene and magnesium. A protein specific to sweet potatoes has been shown to decrease the growth of cancer cells in colorectal carcinoma, tongue cancer and cervical cancer. This unique protease, bikunin, is absorbed intact, unlike most proteins that are broken down into amino acids before being absorbed. Avocados have been shown to improve the absorption of the beta carotene from other vegetables because of their fat content.

Even though there are a lot of ingredients, this salad can be put together rather quickly. When you make grains, always make an extra cup. For a family of four, two cups of grains will allow leftovers most of the time. I use an electric pressure cooker for most grains, but quinoa cooks so quickly I usually just use the stove. For this recipe, I like the sweet potato to be a little firm; it can be microwaved for 4 minutes as you prep the rest of the salad. When you mix avocado and lemon juice with kale, it breaks down some of its fiber, making the kale more tender.

This is a great recovery salad after a hard workout given the complex carbohydrates and multiple sources of significant protein.

Ingredients

- 1/2 bunch leafy kale
- 1 sweet potato, microwaved al dente
- 1 cup cooked quinoa
- 1 cucumber, diced
- 1 orange pepper, diced
- Juice of one lemon
- 1 teaspoon cumin
- 1 teaspoon turmeric
- 1/2 teaspoon cardamom
- Dash of cayenne pepper
- 1/2 avocado
- 1 tablespoon sunflower seeds (hulled, raw unsalted)
- 2 tablespoons raisins

Directions

1. Remove kale stems and chop leaves into small pieces and add to a salad bowl. Save the stems for smoothies or to add to your canine companion's food.
2. Microwave sweet potato for about 4 minutes or boil just enough so a fork pierces it easily.
3. Dice potato and add to the bowl.
4. Add cooked quinoa and mix well.
5. Add diced pepper and cucumber.
6. Dice avocado and add to the bowl.
7. Add spices and lemon juice.
8. Add raisins and sunflower seeds and toss.
9. If you want a little more spice, add a diced hot pepper or a teaspoon of Sriracha sauce.

SERVINGS: 6

PER SERVING: Calories = 145; Total fat = 4g; Total carbohydrates =27g; Protein = 5g; Sodium = 34mg; Fiber = 5g; Iron = 12%

Moroccan Salad

Sushi Salad

I love vegan sushi, but sometimes don't have time to roll my own. A sushi salad is a great way to get in your greens.

Vegan sushi is better than traditional sushi and much safer to eat. There are more and more sushi restaurants offering vegan sushi that is quite beautiful and tasty.

One Saturday after a long run I decided to pick up sushi at my local grocery store, but they were out. Not willing to give up my craving, I realized I had the ingredients in my refrigerator, but not the time to roll out sushi. I decided to add the ingredients to my greens and a great salad was formed! Make extra and it will keep for a few days.

If you keep cooked rice and frozen edamame on hand, you can whip this up easily for lunch. Warm the rice and edamame in the microwave while you prep your vegetables. Edamame are immature or green soybeans, rich in fiber and vitamins and particularly high in folate compared with mature soybeans.

Besides nutrients, inspect your meals for color. How many do you see? Red and yellow peppers and carrots add carotenoids. Green, the color of life, comes from chlorophyll. When you are exposed to sunlight, the potent antioxidant chlorophyll helps to activate CoQ10 in our bodies, which is vital in energy production by our cells and is a great protector of our muscles, including the heart.

Nori sheets are dried seaweed from red algae. They are a good source of iodine that can be limited in a plant-based diet low in iodized salt. Dulse flakes are another sea vegetable that can be added to salads as an iodine source. Cooking beans with a piece of the sea vegetable kombu can be another way to ensure adequate iodine in your diet. The recommended daily allowance for iodine is 150 micrograms. The iodine in 3/8 teaspoon of iodized salt is 150 micrograms and beans contain 19-53 micrograms per ¾ cup. So it is very easy to get adequate amounts of iodine in a plant-based diet as long as you continue to eat a variety of healthy foods.

Ingredients

One container fresh spinach
1 cup diced purple cabbage
2 nori sheets
1 cup cooked edamame
1 tablespoon sesame seeds
1 tablespoon pickled ginger, chopped
1 teaspoon wasabi powder
1 tablespoon lite tamari
2 medium cucumbers, diced
2 medium carrots, shredded
1 avocado, sliced thin
1 cup cooked brown or white rice

Directions

1. Toss spinach, diced cabbage, cucumbers and carrots in a large salad bowl.
2. Add rice, pickled ginger, sesame seeds and wasabi.
3. Cut nori sheets into ribbons and add to the bowl.
4. Add edamame, avocado and tamari and toss.

SERVINGS: 6

PER SERVING: Calories = 150; Total fat = 6g; Total carbohydrates = 19g; Protein = 6g; Sodium = 157mg; Fiber = 6g; Iron = 15%

Sushi Salad

Bok Choy Pomegranate Salad

I use this salad in my introductory nutrition class to demonstrate how fruit and greens can make a beautiful, tasty and nutritious salad. Bok choy is a member of the cabbage family, whose dark green leaves signify an abundance of chlorophyll.

Bok choy is low in oxalates, making it a great nitric oxide-producing vegetable for those with a history of kidney stones. It is also high in folic acid and vitamin B6, which in conjunction with vitamin B12, is important in the metabolism of homocysteine.

Use the whole leaf and stalk to make a crisp, hydrating salad. Adding chopped oranges, lemon juice and pomegranate seeds makes this a super antioxidant salad loaded with vitamin C. It is great anytime, but is especially pretty on a holiday table or buffet.

Pomegranate seeds are also very high in fiber and antioxidants. A diet high in fiber is associated with a decrease in breast cancer, and for every 20 grams of fiber ingested daily, there is an associated 15 percent lower risk of breast cancer. Areas of the world where the fiber intake is over 70 grams also have very little digestive disorders, including colon cancers.

Salad Ingredients
One head bok choy
1/2 cup pomegranate seeds
1/4 cup sliced almonds
1 cup sliced mandarin oranges
Handful of parsley

Dressing
1/4 cup lemon juice
1 tablespoon maple syrup or agave

Directions
1. Chop bok choy into bite-sized pieces and add to a large serving bowl.
2. Slice oranges into small bites and add to the bowl.
3. Add pomegranate seeds.
4, Whisk lemon juice and maple syrup in a small glass bowl then add to the salad.
5. Garnish with sliced almonds.

SERVINGS: 6

PER SERVING: Calories = 84; Total fat = 4g; Total carbohydrates = 12g; Protein = 4g; Sodium = 123mg; Fiber = 3g; Iron = 10%

Bok Choy Pomegranate Salad

Colorful Coleslaw

The basis for any coleslaw is cabbage, one of those super greens full of nitric oxide-producing potential. Cabbage is inexpensive and a great vegetable to have on hand because of its long shelf life. I always have a head of red or green cabbage ready to add to a salad or main dish. Red cabbage contains the most phytonutrients in the cabbage family, and is great for alkalizing the body.

With our Irish heritage, we grew up with the creamy version of coleslaw, so we are presenting a creamy version here. If you prefer the German style, skip the soy yogurt and double the apple cider vinegar. Changing the relish you use will also change the flavor. Try a spicy relish for a kick or a dill relish if sweetness is not your preference.

Remember to check the sodium content of your condiments, taking into account that the vegetables themselves contain sodium. Obviously, fresh vegetables have the lowest sodium content and canned vegetables have the most.

Ingredients

1/2 head red cabbage
1/2 head green cabbage
2 carrots
7 ounces plain soy yogurt
2 tablespoons Dijon mustard
3 tablespoons sweet relish
2 tablespoons fresh parsley
1 teaspoon chili powder
2 tablespoons apple cider vinegar
Black pepper to taste

Directions

1. In a food processor or with a knife, finely chop carrots, red cabbage and green cabbage and place in a large bowl.
2. In a separate bowl, whisk yogurt, mustard and apple cider vinegar and add to the vegetable bowl.
3. Stir in sweet relish.
4. Add chili powder and black pepper and mix thoroughly. Garnish with parsley.

SERVINGS: 6

PER SERVING: Calories = 83; Total fat = 2g; Total carbohydrates = 19g; Protein = 3g; Sodium = 127mg; Fiber = 4g; Iron = 7%

Colorful Coleslaw

Creamy Avocado Potato Salad

This recipe is a great plant-strong substitution for the store-bought potato salad that contains eggs and dairy.

The electric pressure cooker is a great way to cook potatoes quickly. Rinse potatoes in cold water after cooking to make them easier to handle. The sweet relish and mustard in this recipe are good flavor enhancers. I like to use a spicy sweet relish to add a little heat. Some recipes have traditionally used dill relish, so feel free to substitute what you like. German potato salad is vinegar-based so the vinegar in the relish gives this flavor. Depending on your tastes, you can add a little apple cider vinegar to make the dish a little more acidic tasting.

Serving potato salad over a bed of greens adds a nitric oxide source and more fiber. Onions are packed with phytonutrients that are protective against cancer. You can use red or yellow onions, or leeks for those with an onion allergy or those looking for a milder flavor.

When potatoes are cooked and then served cold, their starch becomes more resistant, resulting in a lower glucose spike. People with kidney disease may retain potassium. By peeling the potatoes, boiling, and then discarding the water, the potassium content decreases substantially.

Ingredients

- 1-1/2 pounds small golden potatoes
- 1 ripe Hass avocado
- 2 tablespoons Dijon mustard
- 1/2 diced red onion
- 2-3 tablespoons freshly chopped dill
- 1/4 teaspoon cumin
- 1/2 cucumber, diced
- 1 teaspoon fresh lime juice
- Pepper to taste

Directions

1. Wash and chop potatoes.
3. Boil potatoes for 10-15 minutes, or until they are easily broken apart with a fork.
3. While the potatoes are cooking, blend avocado, dill, mustard, lime juice and cumin in a food processor until smooth. Transfer to a large serving bowl.
4. Add diced cucumber and onion.
5. Rinse cooked potatoes with cold water and transfer to the bowl.
6. Mix thoroughly and add pepper to taste.

SERVINGS: 6

PER SERVING: Calories = 97; Total fat = 3g; Total carbohydrates = 19g; Protein = 2g; Sodium = 216mg; Fiber = 2g; Iron = 4%

Creamy Avocado Potato Salad

Tu-No Salad

Tuna fish salad on toast or on a bed of mixed greens is a favorite meal, so a plant-based option is welcome. This is a hearty recipe for a mock tuna salad that will hold you until dinner, even without the bread. This recipe makes four servings and keeps easily in the refrigerator for a few days. If you want to avoid the seeds, substitute coarsely mashed garbanzo beans.

Ingredients

1 cup raw sunflower seeds, soaked
2 teaspoons light soy sauce
1/3 cup relish
2 teaspoons dulse flakes
1/2 teaspoon paprika
1 tablespoon chopped parsley
1/4 teaspoon onion powder
Pepper to taste
1/3 cup chopped celery

Directions

1. Cover sunflower seeds with 2 cups water and soak overnight.
2. Drain and rinse sunflower seeds and add to a food processor or high-speed blender.
3. Add other Ingredients, plus 1/4 cup water and blend until smooth
4, Add water as needed until you reach a pâté consistency.
5. Serve on sprouted grain bread or on a salad.

Optional sandwich/salad toppings

Spinach
Sliced tomato
Mustard

SERVINGS: 4

PER SERVING: Calories = 228; Total fat = 17g; Total carbohydrates = 14g; Protein = 7g; Sodium = 263mg ; Fiber = 3g; Iron = 12%

Tu-No Salad

Cowboy Caviar

Caviar has never excited me, but this cowboy caviar is something to look forward to. It is very simple, yet nutrient-dense and colorful and loaded with antioxidants and fiber. You can substitute a red onion for the leek, which makes it a little bolder. Leeks are an allium vegetable, as are onions, scallions and garlic. And like onions, if you allow them to sit for at least 5 minutes after cutting them, their nutrients are more readily available. Leeks are a great source of nitric oxide and folate, which makes them very protective from a cardiovascular view.

Ingredients

1 can (12-ounce) black beans
1 can (12-ounce) black-eyed peas
2 cups corn (frozen or fresh)
1 package cherry tomatoes
1 leek, diced
1 large orange bell pepper (or 2 small; you can use yellow, green or red)
1 jalapeño, finely diced
1 avocado, diced
1/3 cup cilantro, chopped
1/3 cup lime juice
1 teaspoon chili powder
1 teaspoon smoked paprika
1 teaspoon cumin
Pepper to taste

Directions

1. Wash vegetables and finely chop leek (or onion), peppers, avocado and cilantro. Wash and quarter cherry tomatoes.
2. Rinse beans and drain well. Thaw frozen corn, if using, and allow to cool completely.
3. In a small bowl, mix lime juice and spices.
4. Add all Ingredients and dressing to a large bowl and toss well.
5. Serve immediately or keep in an airtight container in the refrigerator for up to a week.
6. Serve on its own, over greens or on top of a baked potato.

SERVINGS: 8

PER SERVING: Calories = 227; Total fat = 3g; Total carbohydrates = 46g; Protein = 8g; Sodium = 242mg; Fiber = 6g; Iron = 51%

Cowboy Caviar

Pasta Salad

Pasta salad is one of the most common dishes at a picnic or potluck, but it can be calorie-dense and unhealthy when you add oils, mayonnaise and eggs. Try to make it more about the vegetables than the pasta. You get the biggest nutritional boost from the color in this salad — and no, colored pasta is not a source of nutrients, but a little food coloring or vegetable powder with no more nutritional values than the color on the box it comes in! You can wow your friends and family with this vegetable-, fiber- and nutrient-rich comfort food.

Ingredients

1 box whole wheat or GF rotini pasta
1 bag frozen peas, thawed
1 can organic, low-sodium garbanzo beans
1 cup diced grape tomatoes
2 red bell peppers, diced
3 green onions, chopped
1 cup chopped celery
1 cup chopped carrots
1/2 cup chopped green olives
1/2 cup balsamic vinegar
1/4 cup relish
2 tablespoons Dijon mustard
1 teaspoon onion powder
2 teaspoons garlic powder
1 teaspoon oregano
1 teaspoon basil
Black pepper to taste

Directions

1. Boil pasta until al dente, drain and cool.
2. Chop all vegetables into bite-sized pieces.
3. Mix all Ingredients in a large bowl.
4. Cover and refrigerate until ready to serve.

SERVINGS: 10

PER SERVING: Calories = 227; Total fat = 3g; Total carbohydrates = 46g; Protein = 8g; Sodium = 242mg; Fiber = 6g; Iron = 51%

Pasta Salad

Chapter 4:

Dressings that Look Good and Make You Feel Good

Salads are healthy — until you add dressings that are high in salt, sugar, and fat, bumping up the calorie content to that of a burger and fries.

Here are a few of our simple dressings and a few fancier favorites:

Fresh Salsa with half an avocado

Ginger-Tamari
1 teaspoon lite tamari with 1 tablespoon pickled ginger
1/4 teaspoon wasabi powder
1/2 avocado

Creamy Dill
1/4 cup soy yogurt
1 tablespoon fresh dill
1 tablespoon lemon juice

Blueberry Walnut Vinaigrette
1/2 cup blueberries
1/4 cup walnut halves
1/2 cup balsamic vinegar
Water to thin

SERVINGS: 6

PER SERVING: Calories = 94; Total fat = 3g; Total carbohydrates = 16g; Protein = 1g; Sodium = 7mg; Fiber = 1g; Iron = 4%

Orange-Mango-Ginger Vinaigrette
1 orange
1 box silken tofu
1/2 cup frozen mango, thawed
1 teaspoon ground ginger
1 cup white balsamic vinegar
Blend until smooth.

SERVINGS: 8

PER SERVING: Calories = 95; Total fat = 1g; Total carbohydrates = 15g; Protein = 4g; Sodium = 0mg; Fiber = 1g; Iron = 3%

Creamy Italian
1/2 can low-sodium white beans, drained and rinsed
2 cups nutritional yeast
1/4 teaspoon oregano
1/2 teaspoon basil
1/2 teaspoon garlic
1/2 cup white balsamic vinegar
1/4 teaspoon black pepper
Water to thin
Blend until smooth.

SERVINGS: 6

PER SERVING: Calories = 101; Total fat = 0g; Total carbohydrates = 19g; Protein = 5g; Sodium = 41mg; Fiber = 2g; Iron = 5%

Avocado Citrus
1 avocado
1/2 cup freshly squeezed orange juice

SERVINGS: 1

PER SERVING: Calories = 118; Total Fat = 2g; Total Carbohydrates = 22g; Protein = 4g; Sodium = 12mg; Fiber = 2g; Iron = 6%

Thousand Island
1/2 cup apple cider vinegar
1/4 cup sweet relish
1 box silken tofu
1 tablespoon unsweetened ketchup
Blend until smooth.

SERVINGS: 6

PER SERVING: Calories = 27; Total fat = 1g; Total carbohydrates = 4g; Protein = 1g; Sodium = 99mg; Fiber = 0g; Iron = 2%

Tangy French
1 tablespoon sugar-free ketchup
1 teaspoon Sriracha
1/4 cup white balsamic vinegar
Blend Ingredients, adding water to achieve desired consistency.

SERVINGS: 4

PER SERVING: Calories = 2; Total fat = 0g; Total carbohydrates = 5g; Protein = 0g; Sodium = 61mg; Fiber = 0g; Iron = 0%

Chapter 5:

The Main Attraction: Entrees

Burrito Night

The food of a country is strongly associated with its culture and traditions, as well as being the source of many family memories. The best thing about eating a plant-based diet is that you can create a plant-based version of almost any ethnic dish.

We love burrito night, but when dining out, it can be challenging to get beans and rice without a lot of added oil. The endless baskets of chips, guacamole and salsa can derail a good nutrition plan before the entrée arrives.

Students in my nutrition class always ask, "What do you do for a wrap?" Store-bought wraps are high in fat and preservatives. We have a tasty solution that is quick and easy. Be creative when prepping a variety of toppings to let everyone have their choice to create a colorful, nutrient-dense burrito.

Pinto beans are high in omega-3 fatty acids as well as protein, iron and fiber, but feel free to choose your favorite bean. Consuming beans has been shown to lower heart rate, blood pressure and reduce body weight. Garnishing your burrito with fresh cilantro adds nitric oxide-producing greens for improved vascular function and athletic performance. Making your own fresh salsa instead of using store-bought, jarred salsa means less sodium and preservatives and allows you to control the ingredients. Your fresh salsa will keep several days in the refrigerator, and it is a great topping for salads or baked potatoes.

Salsa with tomatoes, peppers and onions packs vitamin C and antioxidants. The corn tortillas contain fiber and no added oil.

Leftovers can be used for lunches the next day by making extra beans and rice. If you use canned beans, make sure to rinse them thoroughly to remove excess salt, and buy organic when you can to eliminate the potential source of BPA in the can lining. BPA, or bisphenol A, is a synthetic estrogen found in the coating of cans and various containers. It can act like a hormone in the body and has been associated with increased cancer risk and heart disease. It is certainly worth limiting your exposure to this chemical whenever possible. Choosing organic is one way to avoid this, and preparing dried beans yourself is an even better way to control added salt and preservatives.

Ingredients
Tortilla shell
1 cup of instant corn masa (Not corn flour or cornmeal. Masa comes from dehydrated cooked corn.)
11/4 cups water

Filling
1 cup cooked brown rice
2 cans (25-oz each) black or pinto beans or 2 cups dried beans, soaked and cooked
2 medium tomatoes
6 tomatillos
2 jalapeño peppers or hot peppers of your choice
1 cup fresh cilantro
1 teaspoon cumin
1 lime
1 avocado, cut in half and sliced into small wedges

Directions
1. Corn tortillas
2. Mix the corn masa and water in a bowl.
3. Form into 2-inch balls. Press flat between two sheets of parchment paper using a glass bowl and a rolling pin or tortilla press.
4. Peel the tortilla from the paper and place on a hot, dry griddle.
5. Cook each side until slightly brown but still pliable if you want to fold. Otherwise it can be used as an enchilada shell or the base for a burrito bowl.

Salsa Verde
1. Chop tomatoes, tomatillos and 1 jalapeño.
2. Place in the food processor. Add the juice of 1/2 lime and 2 tablespoons chopped cilantro. Add 1/2 teaspoon cumin and blend coarsely.
3. Add contents to a small saucepan and simmer on low until you are ready to assemble the burrito.

Assembly

1. Place a tortilla on a plate.
2. Take 3 slices of avocado and spread over the shell.
3. Add beans and rice. Sprinkle with cumin.
4. Top with salsa verde, a handful of cilantro and more chopped jalapeños.
5. Slide tortilla onto a hot griddle and fold over after 30 seconds.
6. Slide onto a plate, top with more salsa and garnish with cilantro.

SERVINGS: 4

PER SERVING: Calories = 497; Total fat = 7g; Total carbohydrates = 87g; Protein = 19g; Sodium = 265mg; Fiber = 19g; Iron = 26%

Burrito Night

Irish Stew

My dad was Irish, and his mother was a wonderful Irish cook. Her potato soda bread was sought-after for miles around, and she made wonderful meals with food from her garden.

People in the United States associate St. Patrick's Day with corned beef and cabbage. So what's an Irish, plant-based girl to do?

Cabbage is a wonderful and inexpensive nitric oxide-producing vegetable that will dilate your blood vessels, allowing your blood pressure to normalize and your body to be nourished with oxygen and nutrients. Carrots and onions are rich in antioxidants that decrease inflammation and fight cancer. The beans and potatoes are a rich source of protein and fiber.

Ingredients

1/2 head cabbage, chopped
4 medium potatoes, chopped
4 medium carrots, chopped
3 small onions
3 stalks of celery, chopped
1 can butter beans, drained and rinsed
1 tablespoon yellow miso
1 teaspoon black pepper

Slow cooker

Add all Ingredients to a slow cooker, cover with water and cook on high for 6 hours.

Electric pressure cooker

Place all Ingredients in the pressure cooker and cover with an inch of water.
Bring to pressure for 6 minutes then release.
Add the rinsed butter beans, cook on simmer 10 minutes and serve.

We serve this with a side salad of sliced pickled beets, chopped onion and cucumber with apple cider vinegar.

SERVINGS: 4

PER SERVING: Calories = 296; Total fat = 1g; Total carbohydrates = 54g; Protein = 10g; Sodium = 324mg; Fiber = 12g; Iron = 20%

Irish Stew

Cabbage Gnocchi

When Alfreda was first introduced to plant-based nutrition she was beginning chemotherapy for lymphoma. Avoiding animal products helped decrease the potential for infectious bacteria.

It was not easy at first. Her taste buds were damaged by the chemotherapy, and the thought of cooking without animal products, oil or salt was a difficult concept for her to grasp. Being the feisty matriarch of the family, the desire to get well trumped traditional ways of eating, and she began re-creating plant-based versions of old recipes and creating new ones.

She found that adding a little heat with Sriracha or jalapeño peppers helps to decrease the craving for salt, at the same time boosting the flavor. Sauerkraut adds natural probiotics due to the fermentation process. Gnocchi made with whole-wheat pasta and potatoes make this a hearty, filling meal. Cabbage and fresh tomatoes are great additions; however, the acidity of tomatoes denatures the proteins in other vegetables and increases the cooking time, so add the tomatoes last. Add pinto, cranberry or cannellini beans to this dish to make it nutrient-dense and protein-packed.

Ingredients

1 head green cabbage
2 cups sauerkraut
1 package gnocchi
16 ounces tomato purée
1/2 teaspoon pepper
1 jalapeño, diced
1 teaspoon garlic
6 chopped tomatoes or 12-ounce box chopped tomatoes

Directions

1. Chop green cabbage into thin strips and add to a large skillet with a cup of water.
2. Add diced jalapeño, black pepper and garlic and cook until the cabbage is translucent.
3. Add sauerkraut and stir well.
4. When the cabbage is tender, add tomato purée and chopped tomatoes.
5. In a separate saucepan, boil 2 cups water.
6. Add gnocchi to boiling water and cook 5 minutes.
7. Drain gnocchi and add to cabbage mixture.
8. Simmer 10 minutes and serve.

SERVINGS: 6

PER SERVING: Calories = 373; Total fat = 0g; Total carbohydrates = 62g; Protein = 15g; Sodium = 659; Fiber = 17g; Iron = 36%

Cabbage Gnocchi

Garlic Eggplant Stir Fry with Baked Tofu

This Szechuan-inspired dish is one of our go-to Asian meals. Garlic and mushrooms have plenty of cancer-fighting phytonutrients like quercetin, allicin, indoles and glucosinolates. They decrease angiogenesis or blood vessel growth into tumors and cause apoptosis, which is the destruction of tumor cells. Mushrooms also have been shown to counter side effects of chemotherapy such as nausea, bone marrow suppression and anemia. They also have been shown to increase the potency of some chemotherapeutic agents, so be sure and add them to your diet multiple times a week.

Shitake and maitake varieties of mushrooms offer some of the most benefits, but feel free to use the ones you enjoy most. The purple skin of eggplant contains phytonutrients such as resveratrol, anthocyanidins, phenolics and flavonoids. Give this dish a kick with some Thai chili peppers and serve over brown rice to boost your immune system.

Ingredients

4 Chinese eggplant
1 box white mushrooms (you can mix in other types as well)
1 box (14-ounce) firm tofu
5 cloves garlic , minced
1 Thai chili pepper, diced
2 tablespoons light soy sauce
1 teaspoon chopped ginger (fresh or ground)
1/2 cup rice flour
1/2 teaspoon garlic powder
1/2 teaspoon ground ginger
1/2 teaspoon chili powder
1 cup plain, unsweetened plant milk

Directions

1. Preheat oven to 375°F and line a baking sheet with parchment paper.
2. Cube tofu and let it rest on a paper towel to absorb excess moisture.
3. In one bowl, combine the rice flour, garlic powder, ground ginger and chili powder and mix well.
4. In a second bowl, pour 1 cup of plant milk.
5. Dip tofu cubes in the plant milk, then into dry Ingredients. Coat well, then place on baking sheet.
6. Bake 20-25 minutes, until edges are crispy.

Stir Fry Directions

1. Sauté minced garlic in water.
2. Add diced Thai chili pepper and diced eggplant.
3. Add chopped ginger and light soy sauce.
4. Add chopped mushrooms, and cook until tender.
5. Add water as needed to maintain broth.
6. Serve over rice, quinoa or another favorite whole grain.

SERVINGS: 4

PER SERVING: Calories = 269 ; Total fat = 5g ; Total carbohydrates = 36g ; Protein = 15g ; Sodium = 709mg ; Fiber = 13g ; Iron = 23%

Garlic Eggplant Stir Fry with Baked Tofu

Stuffed Shells

Stuffed Shells are one of our family's holiday favorites, and this recipe is one of the more calorie-dense and time-consuming recipes in this book. Therefore, we save it for special occasions. Of course, it is much healthier than the traditional standard American diet version, but it does have more calories and is more likely to result in overindulgence, given the flavor of Italian spices and herbs.

Tofu, also known as bean curd, has a texture similar to ricotta cheese and is naturally high in protein and a good source of calcium. It is often dismissed as being highly processed.

The silken tofu mixed with the garlic, pepper and lemon juice makes a great filling for the shells. My mom's secret ingredient is allspice, which gives the spinach great flavor.

Ingredients
1 box large pasta shells boiled al dente, drained and rinsed with cold water

Stuffing
2 containers silken non-GMO tofu
1 large box fresh spinach, coarsely chopped
1 teaspoon allspice
1/2 teaspoon dry oregano
4 cloves garlic
1/2 teaspoon black pepper
1 tablespoon lemon juice

Sauce
1 large box strained tomatoes
1 large box chopped tomatoes
4 cloves garlic, minced
1 teaspoon dry oregano or 1 tablespoon fresh leaves
1 tablespoon dry basil or 1 handful fresh leaves
1 large box mushrooms, chopped fine
1/2 teaspoon black pepper
1 long hot pepper, minced
1 poblano pepper, chopped fine

Directions

Sauce
1. Sauté minced garlic in a large skillet with 1/4 cup of water and cook on high until garlic starts to shine.
2. Add mushrooms and peppers and continue to stir until the mushrooms release their water.
3. Add chopped and crushed tomatoes and spices and simmer for 20 minutes.

Tofu filling
1. Sauté minced garlic with 1/4 cup of water as above.
2. Add chopped spinach and black pepper and stir until spinach is wilted.
3. Place the silken tofu in a large mixing bowl.
4. Add lemon juice.
5. Add the sautéed spinach, allspice and oregano, and mix thoroughly.

Assembly
1. Preheat oven to 350°F.
2. In a large baking dish, spoon enough sauce to cover bottom of the dish.
3. Using a medium-sized spoon, fill each shell with the tofu mixture and line the baking dish with rows of stuffed shells.
4. After all shells are stuffed and placed in the baking dish, cover them with sauce.
5. Sprinkle with black pepper and bake 30 minutes.

SERVINGS: 6

PER SERVING: Calories = 397; Total fat = 4g; Total carbohydrates = 77g; Protein = 19g; Sodium = 28mg; Fiber = 9g; Iron = 19%

Stuffed Shells

Tempeh Reuben

Reuben sandwiches made the typical way are high in fat, sodium, and are calorie-dense. This version offers the same taste with many healthful benefits. Sauerkraut and tempeh are great probiotics because of their fermentation process. Tempeh has more calories, fiber and protein compared with an equal serving of tofu and gives a heartier flavor to a dish.

We like to serve this on sprouted whole grain bread with tomato and sliced avocado. Limiting sodium can be difficult in traditional recipes, especially if you use prepared ingredients. Always buy plain tempeh and add your own seasonings and rinse sauerkraut or make your own to limit sodium. Choose condiments wisely, looking for one with the lowest sodium content. Adding a little vinegar or water also can decrease the sodium without compromising taste.

Reuben Sauce

1 box (12-ounce) silken tofu
4 teaspoons horseradish (tailored to taste)
1/4 cup plus 1 tablespoon ketchup
3 teaspoons lemon juice
1/4 cup plus 2 tablespoons relish (spicy relish is our favorite)
1/2 teaspoon cayenne pepper

Directions

1. Mix all Ingredients in a food processor until completely blended.
2. Can be stored in the refrigerator for about 1 week.

Reuben Ingredients

Reuben sauce
Tempeh
Sauerkraut

Directions

1. Thinly slice desired amount of tempeh.
2. Rinse sauerkraut to reduce sodium content.
3. Place a few tablespoons Reuben Sauce in a skillet with a small amount of water.
4. Place sliced tempeh and desired amount of sauerkraut on top of sauce and mix in. Heat tempeh and mix all flavors well.
5. Add more Reuben Sauce as desired.
6. Once warmed, scoop the Reuben mixture onto your sandwich or salad.

SERVINGS: 4

PER SERVING: Calories = 224; Total fat = 6g; Total carbohydrates = 27g; Protein = 20g; Sodium = 526mg; Fiber = 7g; Iron = 13% (Bread not included.)

Tempeh Reuben

Plant-powered Pizza

These are not your local pizza joint recipes. Traditional pizza is oily, salty and high-calorie. These traditions are a great way to raise your blood pressure, make your ankles swell, trigger a lower GI earthquake and derail your diet … unless you make it the Dulaney girls' way.

Our plant-strong pizzas are low-stress, taste great, and you won't have to spend the rest of the weekend trying to recover from the effects. You get your dinner serving of nitric oxide-producing greens with sautéed spinach as well as some anti-cancer and anti-inflammatory-packed mushrooms and onions. Don't forget the vitamin C from the tomatoes, zucchini and peppers and the dose of lycopene in the tomato sauce that is great for the prostate. Add some jalapeños and you could reduce your risk of gastric cancers. The whole-wheat crust adds fiber, iron and protein. Pair this with a green salad for extra fiber and nutrients.

Polenta Crust

Ingredients
- 2 cups cornmeal
- 4 cups water

Directions
1. Bring water and cornmeal to a boil in a saucepan.
2. Reduce heat to medium while stirring with a wooden spoon.
3. When the water has absorbed, and it becomes porridge consistency, remove from heat and pour onto a parchment-lined pizza pan.
4. Bake at 450°F or until firm. Add toppings and bake an additional 10-15 minutes until there is no liquid visible on toppings.

SERVINGS: 1 crust

PER SERVING: Calories = 346; Total fat = 1g; Total carbohydrates = 77g; Protein = 7g; Sodium = 5mg; Fiber = 0g; Iron = 0%

Whole Wheat Crust

Ingredients
- 5 cups whole-wheat flour
- 3 teaspoons dry active yeast
- 3 cups water
- 1 teaspoon sugar
- 1/2 teaspoon salt
- 1 tablespoon cornmeal

Directions
1. In a medium-sized mixing bowl, combine 3 cups warm water with yeast and sugar. Stir to dissolve and let rest while preparing dry Ingredients.
2. Mix flour and salt in a large bowl, then add wet Ingredients.
3. Mix until a large dough ball forms that does not stick to the bowl or your hands. Add more flour if sticky.
4. Knead 3 minutes and place the dough ball back in the large bowl. Cover with a warm, wet dishtowel for at least 4 hours.

SERVINGS: 2 crusts

PER CRUST: Calories = 1040; Total fat = 8g; Total carbohydrates = 221; Protein = 40g; Sodium = 594mg; Fiber = 32g; Iron = 60%

This recipe continues...

Plant-powered Pizza

White Sauce

Ingredients
1 can artichokes in water
1 cup fresh basil
4 cloves garlic, chopped
1/4 teaspoon black pepper

Directions
1. Drain artichokes and place in a food processor along with basil, chopped garlic and pepper.
2. Spin until well-mixed and use for a base topping for pizza.

SERVINGS: sauce for 1 pizza

PER SERVING: Calories = 89; Total Fat = 0g; Total Carbohydrates = 17g; Protein = 5g; Sodium = 904g; Fiber = 4g; Iron = 15%

Red Sauce

Ingredients
1 cup unsalted canned tomatoes (I use a box brand that has only tomatoes and no salt added)
1/4 cup tomato paste
1 teaspoon ground basil
1 teaspoon garlic
1/2 teaspoon oregano

Directions
Place Ingredients in a food processor and blend until smooth.

SERVINGS: sauce for 1 pizza

PER SERVING: Calories = 127; Total fat = 0g; Total carbohydrates = 26g; Protein = 7g; Sodium = 52mg; Fiber = 6g; Iron = 14%

Toppings

Ingredients

- 5 cups fresh spinach
- 2 medium zucchini, sliced thin
- 2 cups sliced mushrooms
- 4 cloves garlic
- 1 poblano pepper
- 1 hot pepper (jalapeño or long hot red pepper), chopped fine
- 2 medium tomatoes, sliced thin
- 1/2 cup onion, sliced thin
- 1/2 cup fresh basil
- 1/4 cup chopped green olives
- 1 teaspoon fennel seeds

Directions

1. Chop garlic fine and add to a large skillet with a couple tablespoons of water.
2. Sauté on high heat until the garlic starts to turn golden, stirring so it doesn't stick.
3. Add sliced mushrooms and keep stirring until mushrooms release their water.
4. Add zucchini and sauté until it starts to soften.
5. Add spinach last, folding it into other vegetables as it wilts. Add just enough water to keep things from sticking. Most of the time, however the vegetables release enough moisture to avoid sticking.

Assembly

1. Preheat oven to 475°F
2. Divide dough equally into two balls.
3. For deep-dish pizza, roll out one ball to fit a 12-inch iron skillet. For thin crust, roll the dough to 16 inches for a standard pizza pan or stone.
2. If using a skillet, place the dough in the skillet and add desired sauce.
3. Top with hot vegetables, then cold. Top the sliced tomato with basil leaves.
4. Bake 19 minutes, or until tomatoes appear slightly crusted.
5. Lift the pizza out of the skillet using a large spatula and place on pizza board to serve.

If you choose a thin crust, repeat the above process and bake until the crust is brown.

If using an outdoor grill, coat the pizza pan with cornmeal so the dough slides off easily onto the grill. Bake the crust first, cooking one side for 3 minutes, then flip. Top the cooked side with sauce and fixings, and grill another 4 minutes.

Jackfruit Burger

Everyone is looking for the perfect burger, but a hamburger contributes to a lot to lifestyle diseases with its saturated fat and cell growth factors. The reason the traditional burger is so tempting is not the beef, but the toppings. The salt and fat in those toppings becomes addicting. There are also many chemicals that make the texture of the bun appealing but low in nutrients.

The standard American diet is most lacking in fiber, and the obsession with fast food and burgers is a major contributor. This jackfruit burger is a great way to add fiber and healthy nutrients to a burger.

Jackfruit is a tropical fruit native to India and South America. When harvested young, the pods are not developed and the fibers are dense. It is sold in brine and the sodium content can vary greatly. It is best to rinse the fruit before boiling and then rinse again to remove as much of the sodium as possible. The texture is like that of meat, but much less dense. As with any traditional fruit, it is not calorie-dense, but contains significant amounts of folate, vitamin A and potassium. This makes a very versatile burger when you add different spice combinations. Adding seaweed flakes and a little Old Bay seasoning can even give this burger a crab-like flavor.

Ingredients

- 2 cans jackfruit
- 2 cups oats
- 1/2 lime, squeezed for juice
- Pepper to taste
- 2 tablespoons low-sodium tamari
- 2 teaspoons smoked paprika
- 1 tablespoon garlic powder
- 1 teaspoon cumin

Directions

1. Rinse canned jackfruit well and boil 20 minutes. Drain water and rinse to remove additional sodium.
2. In a large bowl, combine cooked jackfruit and other Ingredients.
3. Form into patties (the recipe makes about 8 large patties), place on a baking sheet, and chill in the freezer for about 20 minutes.
4. Remove from freezer, cook on a non-stick skillet to heat. Serve on a whole-grain bun with vegetables, or on top of a large salad.

SERVINGS: 8

PER SERVING: Calories = 100; Total fat = 2g; Total carbohydrates = 19g; Protein = 4g; Sodium = 139mg; Fiber = 6g; Iron = 18%

Jackfruit Burger

Carrot Dog

Perhaps you are going to a picnic and want something to add to the grill. Maybe you would like a quick meal on a late night. We eat with our eyes first and then our nose. If something looks good and smells good, there's a good chance it will be a family favorite.

Toppings make the traditional hot dog, and the carrot dog is no exception. Sauerkraut is fermented cabbage and loaded with probiotics and nitric oxide-producing arginine. There is nothing better at a picnic than a good carrot dog, and children only need to know it goes great with mustard and ketchup.

Ingredients

8 large carrots, ends trimmed

Marinade

Low-sodium tamari
2 teaspoons smoked paprika
1 tablespoon minced garlic
1 tablespoon yellow mustard
1 teaspoon cumin
Mix Ingredients well.

Directions

1. Boil whole carrots until you can easily pierce them with a fork, or use an electric pressure cooker for 3 minutes.
2. Drain carrots and transfer them to a large glass baking dish or gallon zip bag. Add the marinade to coat the carrots. Marinate overnight in the refrigerator for the best flavor.
3. Cook or grill and top with favorites such as sauerkraut, mustard, relish, ketchup and onions.

SERVINGS: 8

PER SERVING: Calories = 33; Total fat = 0g; Total carbohydrates = 7g; Protein = 1g; Sodium =126mg; Fiber = 2g; Iron = 3%

Carrot Dog

Beet Burger

Beets are great stimulators of nitric oxide production but not everyone has fond memories of their taste. Beets add texture and color to this hearty, nutrient-packed burger without the overwhelming taste of beets.

Ingredients

2 cups beets, shredded
1 can pinto beans
1 cup diced mushrooms
¾ cup cooked quinoa
1/2 cup crushed walnuts
1 teaspoon cumin
1 teaspoon chili powder
1/2 teaspoon smoked paprika
1/2 teaspoon ground fennel

Directions

1. Sauté mushrooms until tender and add to large bowl.
2. Add beans to bowl and mash.
3. Stir in beets, cooked quinoa and spices, then mix well.
4. Add crushed walnuts last. Stir to combine.
5. Make patties and place on a baking sheet lined with parchment paper.
6. Bake at 375°F for 30 minutes or until the outside is crispy.
7. Serve with sliced avocado, lettuce and tomato.

SERVINGS: 8

PER SERVING: Calories = 137; Total fat = 5g; Total carbohydrates = 17g; Protein = 6g; Sodium = 81mg; Fiber = 5g; Iron = 10%

Beet Burger

BBQ Pulled Vork

This is the perfect sandwich for tailgating, BBQs and the Fourth of July! This homestyle pulled "Vork," as Addie's husband, Nathan, has coined it, is yet another twist on tradition. We use our own BBQ sauce to reduce sodium and added sugar intake. Butler's Soy Curls are a one-ingredient plant-based protein alternative that is great to use in soups, casseroles and stews in addition to this smoky sandwich. Make sure to add your colorful greens and vegetables to balance out your plate and enjoy our twist on a traditional BBQ favorite.

Ingredients
- 1 bag (8-ounce) Butler's Soy Curls
- 1 cup homemade BBQ sauce

BBQ Sauce
- 2 tablespoons tomato paste
- 2 tablespoons molasses
- 2 tablespoons maple syrup
- 2 teaspoons turmeric
- 2 teaspoons mustard powder
- 2 teaspoons garlic powder
- 1/2 cup apple cider vinegar
- 1 teaspoon smoked paprika
- Mix Ingredients well.

Directions
1. Place soy curls in a large bowl and cover with water.
2. Let them soak 10 minutes to rehydrate.
3. Drain soy curls and place in a food processor.
4. Using the pulse option, shred the soy curls, but do not purée.
5. Place shredded soy curls in a pot and mix in BBQ sauce.
6. Make sure sauce is mixed well into the soy curls, and marinate for 10 minutes while prepping the rest of your meal.
7. Heat on low to medium heat until warm, then serve.

BBQ Pulled Vork can be eaten on a sprouted bun with sautéed peppers, red cabbage, onions and sprouts, or over a baked potato.

Keep mixture refrigerated in an air-tight container.

SERVINGS: 8

PER SERVING: Calories = 124; Total fat = 4.5g; Saturated fat = 0.5g; Total carbohydrates = 10.75g; Protein = 10.25g; Sodium = 7.4mg; Fiber = 3g

BBQ Pulled Vork

Lentil Loaf

All good vegans eat lentil loaf, our version of meatloaf. And just like your mother's meatloaf, a lentil loaf can have many variations and personal preferences. The bottom line is it is filling and nutritious.

Our family serves lentil loaf with mashed potatoes, green beans and steamed greens such as kale, swiss chard or beet tops, making this meal a powerhouse of nutrients. Cold, sliced lentil loaf is also great for lunch when stuffed in a whole-wheat pita with lettuce and mustard.

Ingredients
1-1/2 cups lentils (plain brown lentils are best)
31/2 cups water
1 onion, diced
2 cloves garlic, minced
4 large carrots, diced
2-3 cups rolled oats (start with the smaller amount, add more as consistency needs)
1/4 cup sugar free ketchup (or BBQ sauce, see page 76)
2 teaspoons garlic powder
1 tablespoon smoked paprika
Black pepper to taste
2 tablespoons fennel seeds (optional)
1/4 cup sugar free ketchup (or BBQ sauce) to coat pan and top loaf

Directions
1. Preheat oven to 350°F. Rinse lentils and drain.
2. Cook lentils in an electric pressure cooker on the bean setting for 36 minutes (no soaking required), or on the stove for 45-60 minutes. They should be very soft and mash easily into the loaf.
3. Drain lentils thoroughly then mash in a large mixing bowl while still hot.
4. In a skillet, sauté onions, carrots and garlic until soft (can be done while lentils are cooking).
5. In a mixing bowl, combine cooked vegetables with mashed lentils and add oats, ketchup or barbecue sauce, and seasonings. Mix well, adding more oats as needed for a thick consistency that's not too wet.
6. Coat a loaf pan with ketchup or BBQ sauce, then gently press the entire lentil mixture into the pan. Drizzle a bit of ketchup or BBQ sauce on top.
7. Bake lentil loaf for 1 hour.
8. Cool slightly before slicing and serving so lentil loaf is firm.

This lentil loaf is even better the next day, and definitely a recipe great to make in advance for busy weeks.

SERVINGS: 12

PER SERVING: Calories = 174; Total fat = 1.4g; Total carbohydrates = 27.5; Protein = 5.7g; Sodium = 166mg; Fiber = 5g

Lentil Loaf

Buddha Bowl

A Buddha bowl gets its name from the story of Buddha carrying his bowl to be filled with whatever bits of vegetarian food local villagers could spare. Today, it represents a balanced meal in one deep bowl. Typically, the vegetables are arranged in sequence or in an artful way to showcase the color of a balanced, plant-based meal. A Buddha bowl can also be a quick, balanced lunch using leftovers.

Fancy bowls can start out healthy, and then a high-calorie, high-fat sauce ruins the concept. We provide a healthy sauce here, but remember that when dining out, you can't always be certain of a sauce's ingredients.

Ingredients

1 cup brown rice
8 cups kale, chopped
4 cups pinto beans, cooked
1 sweet orange pepper, chopped
1 poblano pepper, chopped
1 box portobello mushrooms, chopped
2 cups chopped fresh tomatoes
1 teaspoon garlic powder
1 tablespoon low-sodium tamari
1 tablespoon dehydrated peanut butter
1 teaspoon Sriracha
1 cup water

Directions

1. Cook brown rice and set aside. (I always cook a little extra to have leftovers for lunch.)
2. In a large skillet, sauté kale, peppers and mushrooms with 1/2 cup water and garlic.
3. In a 2-cup measuring cup, mix tamari, 1/2 cup water, peanut butter powder and Sriracha. Set aside.
4. Assemble the Buddha bowls by layering 1/2 cup rice, followed by 1/2 cup cooked beans, then the vegetable mixture.
5. Drizzle the peanut sauce over the bowl and serve.

SERVINGS: 4

PER SERVING: Calories = 162; Total fat = 2.3g; Total carbohydrates = 73.2g; Protein = 21.4; Sodium = 78mg; Fiber = 8g

Buddha Bowl

Eggplant Parmesan

We present to you an eggplant parmesan that stays true to the nutrient-dense purple plant and leaves out all the inflammation. Eggplant is another nutrient-dense vegetable used in many cultural dishes. The deep purple color of this plant provides a rich dose of anthocyanins, one of the many antioxidants responsible for protecting you against free radical damage and disease. Along with the color, eggplant is a wonderful source of fiber, vitamins and minerals.

Eggplant parmesan is a common vegetarian offering at Italian restaurants. Many choose this "healthier" option without considering the side effects of ingredients that coat the eggplant. This dish is typically loaded with parmesan cheese, mozzarella cheese and encrusted in a batter containing processed oil and eggs. The antioxidant properties quickly fall to the wayside once all of these inflammatory ingredients hit your system.

With our plant-strong and dietitian-approved version, you will be enjoying a delicious healthy dose of B12, plant-based protein, healing herbs and spices and the beautiful benefits of eggplant! Eggplant parmesan can be eaten alone or paired with your favorite pasta and marinara sauce.

Plant-based parmesan Ingredients

3 tablespoons nutritional yeast
1/2 teaspoon garlic powder
1/2 cup raw cashews

Directions

1. Add all Ingredients to a food processor and blend to a fine powder.
2. Refrigerate in an airtight container or jar for a couple of weeks.

Eggplant Parmesan Ingredients

1 eggplant
1/4 cup flour
1 cup breadcrumbs
2 tablespoons homemade parmesan
1 teaspoons dried oregano
1/2 cup unsweetened plain plant-based milk
1 tablespoon cornstarch
Your favorite pasta and marinara sauce

Directions

1. Slice eggplant thin and place slices on paper towels. Cover slices with another layer of paper towels and top with a heavy object to draw out moisture. Let sit for 10-15 minutes.
2. Preheat oven to 400°F and make your dipping stations. You will need one bowl containing plant-based milk mixed with cornstarch and the other bowl containing blend of flour, breadcrumbs, salt, oregano and homemade parmesan.
3. Line baking sheets with parchment paper.
4. Dip eggplant slices in the liquid bowl, then the dry bowl, then place on the baking sheets.
5. Bake eggplant for 30 minutes or until brown. While the eggplant in finishing, begin to heat pasta and marinara.
6. When eggplant is done, remove from the oven and serve with pasta and marinara.

SERVINGS: 4

PER SERVING: Calories = 169 ; Total Fat = 4g ; Total Carbohydrates = 29g ; Protein = 6g ; Sodium = 43mg ; Fiber = 6g ; Iron = 8%

Eggplant Parmesan

Chapter 6:

Satisfying Sides

Traditional American side dishes are such foods as baked potatoes, green beans, and corn. More broadly, they were a vegetable and starch to complete the plate. When the whole plate is from plant foods, it can be hard to pair foods to make a nutritionally complete plate. The sides we have chosen can be paired quite easily and even repurposed for lunch the next day.

When we think of a healthy, nutritionally complete plate, we like to see leafy greens, colorful vegetables, starches, and beans. Below are sides that will make your healthy plate complete.

Baked Beans

Almost everyone loves baked beans. But store-bought beans are loaded with sodium and sugar, not to mention animal products. This home-style version is a crowd-pleaser, even for those who are not plant-strong. They are a great covered dish for a cookout and pair well with veggie burgers and potatoes. With this recipe, you don't have to miss out on a BBQ favorite.

Ingredients

1 cup cooked pinto beans
1 cup cooked black beans
1 cup cooked lima beans
1 cup liquid reserved from cooking beans
1 tablespoon tomato paste
1 tablespoon Dijon mustard
2 teaspoons apple cider vinegar
3 teaspoons maple syrup
1 tablespoon molasses
2 teaspoons garlic powder
2 teaspoons smoked paprika

Directions

1. Combine all cooked, drained beans in a large bowl
2. In a separate bowl, blend remaining Ingredients well to make sauce.
3. Pour sauce over beans and mix well.
4. Transfer beans to a baking dish, and bake at 350°F for 30 minutes.

SERVINGS: 6

PER SERVING: Calories = 118, Total fat = 1.5g; Total carbohydrates = 18g; Protein = 6.8g; Sodium = 25.8mg; Fiber = 8.8 g

Baked Beans

Loaded Baked Potato

This loaded baked potato is a meal in itself. Add some greens and you are plant-strong! The baked potato base is a perfect way to repurpose leftover beans and corn. It is also a great quick lunch if you wrap the potato in a dish towel and microwave 6 minutes on high or until tender.

You can also convert this recipe to an appetizer by using small potatoes, loaded and placed on a platter.

Ingredients

1 baked potato, cooked
1/2 cup beans
Fresh salsa
1/4 avocado
Spices: chili powder, garlic powder, cayenne pepper, smoked paprika and/or nutritional yeast

Directions

1. Add cooked potato to large bowl of fresh greens of your choice.
2. Top potato with beans, salsa, sliced avocado and spices of your choice.
3. Mix all Ingredients and enjoy!

SERVINGS: 1

PER SERVING: Calories = 280, Total fat = 4.5g; Total carbohydrates = 51g; Protein = 9g; Sodium = 260mg; Fiber = 13g

Loaded Baked Potato

Sunflower Seed Rice Balls

These are a great addition to pasta and a vegetable-rich marinara sauce and add protein, magnesium, fiber and iron. The key ingredient to making an Italian-flavored meatball or sausage is fennel seed. Fresh parsley also gives this seed ball the taste of traditional meatballs. Bake and add sauce on top rather than simmer in the sauce to ensure consistency in the texture.

Ingredients

1 cup sunflower seeds, soaked 4 hours
1 cup cooked short-grain brown rice
2 teaspoons ground fennel seeds
1 teaspoon cumin
1 teaspoon garlic
3 tablespoons chopped fresh parsley
1/2 teaspoon pepper
1/4 teaspoon oregano
1 tablespoon low-sodium tamari

Directions

1. Preheat oven to 350°F.
2. Rinse sunflower seeds and drain.
3. Add seeds to food processor and process until coarsely ground. Transfer to a large mixing bowl.
4. Add cooked rice to the food processor and process just until coarsely chopped. Transfer to the same mixing bowl.
5. Add fennel seeds, cumin, garlic, parsley, pepper, oregano and tamari.
6. Mix well and form into 1-1/2- to 2-inch balls and place on a parchment-lined baking sheet.
7. Bake 30 minutes and serve with tomato sauce.

Note: Do not simmer balls in sauce because they will degrade.

SERVINGS: 12 balls

PER SERVING: Calories = 100, Total fat = 8.8g; Total carbohydrates = 7.4g; Protein = 4g; Sodium = 6.3mg; Fiber = 1.3g

Sunflower Seed Rice Balls

Baked Coconut Tofu

People new to the plant-based or vegan lifestyle worry about the source of tofu. Soymilk is congealed with a binder such as calcium phosphate and pressed into a block. The firmness depends on the binder.

It has very little taste if not seasoned, but is very versatile when seasoned or marinated. Think of tofu as a bean, in that it adds extra protein and calories to a meal. The phytoestrogens are often a source of controversy or fear. In fact, they block the estrogen receptors in the body, making them protective against breast and prostate cancer.

Baking tofu is a great way to get it crunchy on the outside and soft on the inside. Serve with a vegetable stir fry or use as an appetizer. Make some to have left over and reheat as a snack for the kids after school.

Ingredients

- 1 box firm non-GMO tofu
- 1/2 cup unsweetened coconut flakes
- 1 flaxseed egg
- 1 tablespoon light tamari
- 3 tablespoons water

Directions

1. Prepare the flaxseed egg by combining 1 tablespoon ground flaxseed with 3 tablespoons water and let rest for 10 minutes.
2. Drain tofu well and press by placing a heavy saucepan on top for 10 minutes.
3. Cube tofu block with 4 horizontal and 3 vertical cuts.
4. Mix tamari and water and add cubed tofu so the tofu is covered.
5. Place shredded coconut in a zip bag.
6. Dip the tofu into the flaxseed egg mixture to coat.
7. Place 5 pieces of flaxseed-coated tofu at a time into the zip bag and coat with coconut.
8. Place coconut-coated tofu on a parchment-lined baking sheet.
9. Bake at 375°F for 30 minutes or until coconut is lightly browned.

SERVINGS: 12

PER SERVING: Calories = 59; Total fat = 5.6g; Total carbohydrates = 2.5g; Protein = 3.9; Sodium = 51mg; Fiber = 1.6g

Baked Coconut Tofu

Omega Balls

This recipe is yet another option to add to pasta in addition to a vegetable-rich marinara. The focus of many of the ingredients below is that they are rich sources of omega-3 fatty acids. From the pinto beans to the walnuts and chia seeds, these Omega Balls will be contributing anti-inflammatory nutrients to your meal. This is quite opposite of the pro-inflammatory animal protein-based meatballs typically served on pasta nights. The fennel seeds are a traditionally used spice in sausage, giving this recipe familiar flavors.

Ingredients

1 can pinto beans (organic and low-sodium whenever possible)
1 cup rolled oats
2 tablespoons whole fennel seeds
1 tablespoon fresh basil
1/4 cup walnuts
2 tablespoons chia seeds plus 6 tablespoons warm water
1/4 cup nutritional yeast
2 teaspoons garlic powder
Black pepper to taste

Directions

1. Preheat oven to 375°F and line a baking sheet with parchment paper.
2. Soak chia seeds plus warm water in a small bowl and set aside to congeal while prepping the rest of the Ingredients.
3. Combine oats, fennel seeds, basil and walnuts in a food processor and blend into a fine powder consistency. Pour blended Ingredients into a separate mixing bowl.
4. Blend the rinsed pinto beans plus 1/4 cup water in a food processor until you have a smooth but thick consistency. Add beans to mixing bowl.
5. Add remaining spices and chia seed mixture to the mixing bowl and combine ALL Ingredients (using a spoon or your hands) until consistent dough is formed.
6. Form small balls and place on baking sheet.
7. Bake about 15 minutes, or until outer edges are slightly brown and firm.
8. Add Omega Balls to any pasta dish, salad or sandwich in place of meatballs.

SERVINGS: 12

Calories = 96 ; Total fat = 3g ; Total carbohydrates = 13g ; Protein = 5g ; Sodium = 41 mg ; Fiber = 4g ; Iron = 8%

Omega Balls

Garden Cornbread Muffins

You may have heard muffins called cupcakes without icing. They are indeed quite alike if made traditionally with oil and sugar. Most muffin mixes use white flour with a little corn flour or cornmeal for flavor, thus creating a high-fat, low-fiber food. Growing up, my grandmother made cornbread with home-grown corn that was milled by hand.

There were also a lot of ingredients I won't mention that made them very fatty and calorie-dense. We would then top them with jelly and butter, making it even worse.

We know better now that we can enjoy a corn muffin without all of those unhealthy ingredients.

Ingredients

1 hot pepper, chopped fine
1 red bell pepper, chopped fine
2 cups fresh spinach
1 cup fresh cooked or frozen corn
1 cup cornmeal
1-1/2 cups corn flour
1-1/2 teaspoons baking soda
1/4 cup applesauce
3 tablespoons maple syrup
1 cup fresh salsa
1/2 cup plain almond milk

Directions

1. Preheat oven to 400°F. Lay out a non-stick muffin tin.
2. In a skillet, lightly sauté spinach, peppers and corn 5 minutes.
3. In a large bowl, blend together all dry ingredients.
4. Add wet Ingredients and cooked vegetables to the bowl. Mix well.
5. Spoon batter into muffin tin and bake 25 minutes.
6. Cool slightly, and remove muffins from tin.
7. Serve and enjoy!

SERVINGS: 12 muffins

PER SERVING: Calories = 132; Total fat = 1.2g; Total carbohydrates = 21.2g; Protein = 2.6g; Sodium = 26mg; Fiber = 2.5g

Garden Cornbread Muffins

Sweet Potato Falafel

Falafel is sometimes referred to as Israeli street food. Original falafel contained fava beans as well as chickpeas, but an enzymatic deficiency among some Jewish people resulted in a potentially lethal reaction. This led to using only chickpeas in most recipes from Israel.

Cilantro and parsley are two other original ingredients that are great nitric oxide producers.

We add sweet potato, which gives a slightly sweet taste and loads of beta carotene known to decrease wet macular degeneration as well as colon cancer recurrence. Sprinkling some whole wheat panko breadcrumbs before baking makes the falafels crispy on the outside and allows them to hold up with a soy yogurt-based dill sauce. We enjoy serving this with tabbouleh.

Ingredients

1 medium sweet potato, boiled or baked
1 can (15-ounce) chickpeas, drained and rinsed
2 cloves garlic, finely minced
1/2 cup fresh parsley, chopped
1/2 teaspoon pepper
Sesame seeds for garnish

Directions

1. Preheat oven to 350°F and line a baking sheet with parchment paper.
2. Remove the skin of the sweet potato and mash in a large bowl, using a fork or potato masher.
3. Place chickpeas in a food processor, blend coarsely and add to the mashed sweet potato.
4. Add garlic, parsley and pepper and mix well.
5. Spoon the mixture onto the baking sheet. Use a large spoon to make patties about 2 inches in diameter.
6. Top with sesame seeds and bake 40 minutes.

SERVINGS: 8

PER SERVING: Calories = 74; Total fat = 1g; Total carbohydrates = 13g; Protein = 3g; Sodium = 73mg; Fiber = 3g; Iron = 5%

Sweet Potato Falafel

Poblano Pepper and Potato Casserole

My Noonie is the master of creating a recipe by simply looking in her refrigerator and pantry and using the ingredients on hand.

This Poblano Pepper and Potato Casserole was a spontaneous creation from Alfreda's kitchen that has become a family favorite. Unlike traditional casseroles that are often high in sodium and fat, this recipe is nutrient-dense. It can be paired with seasoned beans and greens to make a balanced and satisfying meal that is also easy and quick to create.

Ingredients

2 poblano peppers, sliced thin
1 onion, diced
4 medium potatoes
2 medium zucchini, sliced thin
1 box mushrooms, sliced thin
1 tablespoon arrowroot or cornstarch
Black pepper to taste
1 tablespoon miso

Directions

1. Boil potatoes until you can stick a fork in them or cook 3 minutes in the Instant Pot. Slice thin and arrange in a large baking dish.
2. Sauté onion, zucchini, peppers and mushrooms in a large skillet with a 1/2 cup of water.
3. Add vegetables to potatoes.
4. Mix miso and black pepper in a cup of water and add to baking dish.
5. Add arrowroot or cornstarch to 1/2 cup water and mix well. Add to the baking dish to make a broth.
6. Bake for 30 minutes at 350°F.

SERVINGS: 6

PER SERVING: Calories = 118 ; Total Fat = 1g ; Total Carbohydrates = 26g ; Protein = 4g ; Sodium = 121mg ; Fiber = 4g ; Iron = 7%

Poblano Pepper and Potato Casserole

Deviled Tomatoes

Deviled eggs: Every covered dish dinner and potluck has 'em.

They are finger foods that are cholesterol-rich and full of saturated fat and never get reported on a food log. Deviled tomatoes, on the other hand, are a nutrient-dense, antioxidant-rich food. They can be enjoyed by everyone, which makes them a great offering for a covered-dish event. To reduce food waste, save the scooped-out portion of the tomatoes to use as a base for soup.

Ingredients

1 can (15-ounce) chickpeas, drained and rinsed
1 box (14-ounce) silken tofu
2 tablespoons nutritional yeast
1 tablespoon lemon juice
2 tablespoons Dijon mustard
1 teaspoon turmeric
1 teaspoon cumin
1 teaspoon curry powder
1/4 teaspoon black pepper
2 tablespoons chopped chives or cilantro
12 ripe plum tomatoes
Sweet paprika for garnish
1 bunch romaine lettuce

Directions

1. Place the first 9 Ingredients in the food processor and blend until smooth.
2. Cut plum tomatoes in half and scoop out the center. (Save the centers for soups or sauces.)
3. Stuff the remaining tomato halves with generous portions of the chickpea mixture and sprinkle with paprika and top with scallions or cilantro.
4. Arrange on a bed of romaine or leafy greens for a nice presentation.

SERVINGS: 12

PER SERVING: Calories = 63; Total fat = 0.7g; Total carbohydrates = 8.8g; Protein = 4.8g; Sodium = 16.3mg; Fiber = 1.6g

Deviled Tomatoes

Polenta

Polenta, made from coarsely milled dried corn, is a versatile addition to many dishes that also can be eaten for breakfast as corn porridge. It has been a staple in a variety of ethnic cultures from Kenya to Italy to Eastern Europe to the Southern United States.

Corn has received a bad rap for being associated with genetically modified livestock feed and high-fructose corn syrup. Organic cornmeal is GMO-free and a good source of fiber, protein and carbohydrates. It contains carotenoids as well as vitamin A.

Corn is also a source of iron, magnesium and zinc, helping you to meet your daily nutritional requirements. This polenta can be eaten as is, or topped with chili or other vegetables. You can also add flavors by adding fresh herbs and sundried tomatoes while cooking.

Ingredients

- 1 cup cornmeal
- 3 cups water

Directions

1. Boil water in a medium saucepan.
2. Add cornmeal and stir with a wooden spoon until the mixture comes to a boil. Reduce heat to medium and stir until the mixture thickens like porridge. This takes about 5 minutes.
3. Pour into a loaf pan or 8 x 8-inch glass baking dish and let stand.
4. Slice and serve with chili or sautéed greens.

SERVINGS: 6

PER SERVING: Calories = 442; Total fat = 0.7g; Total carbohydrates = 15.6g; Protein = 1.7g; Sodium = 7.1g; Fiber = 1.5g

Noonie's Thanksgiving Stuffing Balls

Some traditional holiday foods of the standard American diet have obviously been passed along without thoughts of food safety or nutrition. If you are looking for a way to soak up saturated fat from animal fat, then traditional stuffing serves that purpose. On the other hand, if you would like to keep some of the nutritional traditions of Thanksgiving without the dire health consequences, then Noonie's stuffing balls are a guaranteed winner. We win folks over with these in nutrition classes every year. There is comfort knowing you can still maintain holiday traditions and eat healthy.

Unlike traditional stuffing, these balls contain fiber, antioxidants and omega-3 fatty acids without the saturated fat.

Ingredients

1 loaf Ezekiel bread, or whole wheat bread without oil or preservatives, cut into cubes
1 tablespoon ground flaxseed plus 3 tablespoons water
1/2 teaspoon black pepper
1 cup finely chopped celery
1 cup finely chopped onion or leeks
2 cups warm vegetable broth or aquafaba from cooked chickpeas
2 tablespoons miso

Directions

1. Preheat oven to 350° F and line a baking sheet with parchment paper.
2. Mix all Ingredients in a large bowl. Form into balls and place on the baking sheet.
3. Bake 30 minutes or until slightly browned.

These go well with Marvelous Mushroom Gravy.

SERVINGS: 12

PER SERVING: Calories = 161; Total fat = 1.4g; Total carbohydrates = 5.4g; Protein = 7.4g; Sodium = 286mg; Fiber = 5.7g

Noonie's Thanksgiving Stuffing Balls

Chapter 7:

Sensational Sauces

Sauces have become synonymous with covering up poor-quality ingredients to make them taste good. In reality, today's sauces make everything taste much the same. In fact, there are many unhealthy ingredients in jarred and restaurant sauces as well added sugar, oil and salt.

Portion sizes on labels are often unrealistic and ignored when looking at the total calorie count of a meal. My mother is the matriarch of tomato sauce in our house. Addie and I have added our touches to the sauce, but it is mom who wears the crown.

Many people have been raised on food prepared in olive oil or butter. These oils cover the taste of the vegetables and cloud taste buds. When they are omitted, people sense something is missing. In reality, the taste of the spices and vegetables now move forward and provide many new flavor combinations. Try to taste the different herbs in your sauces. Compare fresh herbs with dried herbs. There are many varieties of curries and paprika that can provide unique flavors to your sauces.

This chapter features some of our favorite sauces and secret ingredients that we hope you will enjoy.

Savory Butternut Squash Sauce

This is a savory sauce that goes great tossed with kale. Adding a whole grain or wild rice is a nice addition as well. This is a beta carotene-packed dish that tastes like you are indulging in a rich creamy sauce, but is not calorie- or fat-dense. Adding more nutritional yeast will give the sauce a more cheesy taste, and adding a little more cumin and turmeric will make it a more savory sauce. Addie takes the helm with this sauce and makes it a hearty meal for the athlete, including her collegiate strength coach husband, Nathan. She does this by combining it with sautéed greens, like kale, and pouring it over a lentil based pasta.

Ingredients

1 butternut squash
1 tablespoon chopped garlic
1 tablespoon soy sauce
2 teaspoons lemon juice
2 tablespoons apple cider vinegar
3 tablespoons nutritional yeast
2 teaspoons cumin
1 tablespoon smoked paprika
¾ cup plain almond milk

Directions

1. Slice and dice butternut squash.
2. Boil diced squash and garlic in a large pot of water, cook until the squash is very tender.
3. Add squash and about 2 cups of the cooking water to a blender.
4. Add vinegar and almond milk and blend until smooth.
5. Add remaining spices to taste.

SERVINGS: 6

PER SERVING: Calories = 73; Total fat = 0.4g; Total carbohydrates = 16.4g; Protein = 3.6g; Sodium = 107mg; Fiber = 3g

Savory Butternut Squash Sauce

Cauliflower Alfredo

Who says you can't have Alfredo sauce without the inflammatory side effects? Cauliflower is a nitric oxide powerhouse and is as versatile as it is nutrient-dense. The key to creaminess is getting the cauliflower well- cooked and then well-drained. Garlic and nutritional yeast give this great flavor. I love this sauce over sautéed mushrooms, red peppers and asparagus. Serve with a whole grain as a complete meal.

Ingredients

1 head cauliflower, cut into florets
1/4 cup nutritional yeast
2 teaspoons garlic powder
1 cup unsweetened nut milk
Black pepper

Directions

1. In a pressure cooker or pot, cover cauliflower with water. Boil or pressure-cook until well-done. Pressure-cook time is 4 minutes.
2. Drain water and add nutritional yeast, garlic and nut milk.
3. Blend until smooth with a hand blender. Alternatively, transfer cauliflower to a blender, add remaining Ingredients and blend until smooth.
4. Add additional nut milk for desired thickness, and black pepper to taste.

SERVINGS: 6

PER SERVING: Calories = 48; Total fat = 0.5g; Total carbohydrates = 8g; Protein = 4g; Sodium = 51mg; Fiber = 3g

Cauliflower Alfredo

Tangy Yellow Tomato Sauce

There are sauces you pour over food and sauces you mix with food. This is a sauce that looks beautiful under your vegetables. Yellow tomatoes are tangier than red tomatoes, and also have a slightly different nutritional profile, so adding both red and yellow tomatoes is a great way to make your sauces nutritional powerhouses.

While they have the same protein and calorie content, yellow tomatoes have slightly less fiber but almost twice the daily RDA for iron and zinc as red tomatoes. Yellow tomatoes have more sodium at 43mg versus 11mg, but the sodium is still low when you are not adding salt to your recipes. They have twice the niacin and folate but slightly less vitamin c and lycopene.

Sodium can add up with condiments, so watch the sodium content of the mustard you purchase. Mustard also enhances the anti-cancer phytonutrients in cruciferous vegetables, so think about mustard or mustard powder when you are making these dishes.

Adding turmeric and ginger makes this sauce an antioxidant powerhouse. We use pearl couscous with this dish, but you can substitute wild rice or pearl barley. Our choices for greens in this dish are broccoli, broccolini, asparagus or a combination. Broccolini is a hybrid vegetable developed in 1993 from broccoli and Chinese broccoli. It is more tender and slightly sweeter than broccoli, in my opinion.

Ingredients

- 4 yellow tomatoes, quartered
- 2 tablespoons Dijon mustard
- 1 teaspoon turmeric
- 1 teaspoon ginger
- 2 tablespoons apple cider vinegar

Directions

1. Place quartered tomatoes in the blender and blend on high until smooth. Add contents to a large skillet or saucepan
2. Add Dijon mustard, turmeric, ginger and apple cider vinegar and simmer for 20 minutes.

This sauce is excellent as a base for Israeli couscous or pearl barley. Serve with sautéed mushrooms and your favorite nitric oxide-producing greens.

SERVINGS: 6

PER SERVING: Calories = 18; Total fat = 0.2g; Total carbo-hydrates = 3.8g; Protein = 1g; Sodium = 52mg; Fiber = 1g

Tangy Yellow Tomato Sauce

Vegetable-Rich Marinara

Pasta night is always a great night in the Dulaney household.

The smells of garlic, basil and oregano tell the story. The sauce is not too thick, yet not too thin. Every Italian family has a different tomato sauce recipe. Some Italians call their sauce gravy, but when you also share Irish heritage, gravy means a savory brown sauce.

My mother's secret ingredients in her tomato sauce are allspice and red pepper. There is more than a little heat in this sauce, but you can still taste the other herbs and spices. Tomato sauce is a great way to add vegetables to your dinner. If your family likes vegetables, just sauté garlic and mushrooms and add other vegetables before the tomatoes. If there are picky eaters in your house, you can puree the vegetables so they are not discovered. Dicing mushrooms very fine will give them a meaty texture.

You can always go with traditional marinara sauce and serve the vegetables on the side. Whether they are mixed in with the sauce or on the side, vegetables play an important role in the nutritional density of a meal. The focus should be on the vegetables and sauce with the pasta playing less of a leading role. This decreases the caloric density of the meal.

For those looking for a more hearty meal, add the Sunflower Seed Rice Balls featured on page 90 or the Omega Balls featured on page 94.

Ingredients

1 box crushed tomatoes (preferably without salt or additives)
1 box strained tomatoes
5 cloves garlic, minced
1 long, green hot pepper (or poblano pepper for a milder sauce), diced
1 teaspoon oregano
1 teaspoon allspice
1 teaspoon basil
1/4 teaspoon black pepper
2 medium zucchini, chopped
2 cups chopped mushrooms
3 cups or more fresh spinach
1 tablespoon fresh basil

Directions

1. Add 1/4 cup water to a large skillet or saucepan and sauté the garlic, mushrooms and diced hot pepper until mushrooms have released their juices.
2. Add zucchini and spices and stir until zucchini is tender.
3. Add spinach and stir until it wilts.
4. Add tomatoes and basil and simmer 30 minutes.
5. Add black pepper to taste.

Serve with your favorite pasta and a big green salad.

SERVINGS: 6

PER SERVING: Calories = 103; Total fat = 0.6g; Total carbohydrates = 20g; Protein = 5g; Sodium = 34mg; Fiber = 6.4g

Vegetable-Rich Marinara

Marvelous Mushroom Gravy

Changing your nutrition to improve your health occurs more often because you need to rather than because you want to. Perhaps your physician or family members suggested it, and you have agreed to give it a go.

I had such a patient, who was truly trying to change his nutrition, but confided in me that he did not enjoy the food, as it was nothing like he was used to eating. Looking for common ground, I asked him if he liked mashed potatoes. His eyes lit up, but he hesitated, and said, "I like gravy on my mashed potatoes and I cannot have that anymore."

I told him about mushroom gravy and he was intrigued. The next time he came back to the office, he was doing much better and was much happier. He said the mushroom gravy was a game-changer. The recipe gave him hope that he could have food that was familiar to him.

Sometimes it just takes just one favorite recipe to change the view of plant-based nutrition from a way you have to eat to a way you enjoy to eat. Our family enjoys each meal. We have developed new favorites, but we also like to tweak our standards to make them even better.

Mushroom gravy can be different depending on the mushroom varieties you choose. I like to combine three or four varieties for a host of different flavors and textures.

Ingredients

2 boxes portobello mushrooms, chopped fine
1 box shitake mushrooms, chopped fine
4 cloves garlic, minced
Black pepper
1 tablespoon tapioca flour dissolved in 2 tablespoons of water

Directions

1. Heat a large skillet on high and add garlic and 1/4 cup water. Stir for about a minute until the garlic becomes golden.
2. Add 1/2 cup water and the chopped mushrooms and continue to stir until the mushrooms release their moisture.
3. Add 2 cups water and drop the temperature to medium, allowing the mushrooms to generate a broth. Continue to add small amounts of water as the mushrooms thicken.
4. Add the dissolved tapioca flour to the mushroom mixture and stir until it thickens.
5. Serve over mashed potatoes or polenta.

SERVINGS: 10

PER SERVING: Calories = 19; Total fat = 0g; Total carbohydrates = 4g; Protein = 2g; Sodium = 4mg; Fiber = 1g; Iron = 2%

Marvelous Mushroom Gravy

Green Power Pesto Sauce

Are you looking for a tasty sauce loaded that is also loaded with nitric oxide generating potential? This sauce is naturally low in calories but rich in flavor. Serve this sauce as a base topped with tempeh and a whole grain.

Ingredients

1 large box spinach (about 5 cups)
1 bunch of cilantro (or basil)
1/4 cup cashews
1 jalapeño pepper, diced
4 cloves garlic, finely minced
1/4 teaspoon cayenne pepper
1/2 teaspoon garam masala
Juice of one lemon

Directions

1. In a Vitamix or other high-speed blender, add spinach, 2 cups water and lemon juice. Blend until smooth.
2. Add cashews and jalapeño. Blend on high speed for 2-3 minutes.
3. Add the cayenne, garlic and lemon juice and blend on high until the mixture warms in the blender.
4. Transfer to a skillet and let simmer for 15 minutes.
5. Serve by plating the sauce followed by a grain of your choice and grilled vegetables.

This sauce is great with polenta, quinoa or other whole grains.

SERVINGS: 6

PER SERVING: Calories = 36; Total fat = 2.0g; Total carbohydrates = 2.5g; Protein = 1.8g; Sodium = 24mg; Fiber = 1.2g

Green Power Pesto Sauce

Potato CheeZ Sauce

The days when mac 'n cheese left you feeling guilty are over!

This 100% whole food, plant-based, "cheeZ" sauce is creamy, savory, nutrient-dense, low-calorie and cholesterol-free. The potato base of this sauce provides fiber, plant-based protein, vitamin B6, vitamin C, potassium, magnesium and iron.

Since the sauce is potato-based, I love to pair it with a lentil/chickpea-based pasta and a colorful green like broccoli or collards to keep the meal balanced.

Ingredients

6 russet potatoes (small to medium)
1/2 cup raw cashews
1/2-1 cup plain, unsweetened almond milk
1 tablespoon miso paste
1 tablespoon plus 1 teaspoon apple cider vinegar
1/4 teaspoon cumin
1 tablespoon minced garlic (or 2 teaspoons garlic powder)
3 teaspoons nutritional yeast
Smoked paprika (optional, for a smokier sauce)

Directions

1. Soak cashews for at least 2 hours. If you forget to soak, simply cover with water and bring to a boil on the stove. Cook until you can pierce cashews with a fork.
2. Wash and peel potatoes. Dice and place in an Instant Pot. Add 2 cups of water (so they are not completely covered), close lid and select manual setting for 10 minutes.
3. Once potatoes are cooked, transfer potatoes and liquid into a high-speed blender. Add cooked cashews and begin blending.
4. Add almond milk, vinegar, miso, garlic and spices.
5. Blend until smooth.
6. Add more almond milk or water if needed for consistency.

Serve over vegetables and greens paired with whole-wheat pasta, a lentil/legume-based GF pasta, rice, or as a whole-food, plant-based fondue.

SERVINGS: ~10

PER SERVING: *Calories = 100; Total fat = 2g; Total carbohydrates = 19g; Protein = 4g; Sodium = 86mg; Fiber = 2g*

Potato CheeZ Sauce

Chapter 8:

Noonie-Approved Soups

"Soup is comfort food to me. It warms and heals."
Alfreda Dulaney

Alfreda is the creator of many of the soups we have invented or reinvented as plant-based. These soups are colorful, nutrient-dense and filling. Adding a whole grain can increase the caloric density of the soups. Serving over polenta or a baked potato is another way to add heartiness.

Green Goddess Soup

Green is good, and this soup is no exception. Need to get some extra nitric oxide-producing greens in your diet today? Do you have more greens in the refrigerator than you know what to do with? Then this recipe is your solution. My favorite greens to add in this soup are mustard greens, but they are not always available. Bok choy adds a lot of flavor as well. Peas and carrots give this soup additional beauty, but if you don't like peas, add white beans, edamame, or even tofu cubes.

Ingredients

- 3 cups mustard greens, chopped (or other greens of your choice)
- 2 stalks celery, finely chopped
- 2 large carrots, finely chopped
- 1 tablespoon miso
- 1 can navy beans, drained and rinsed
- 4 medium potatoes, chopped
- 2 cloves garlic, finely chopped
- 1/2 jalapeño pepper, diced
- 1 box white mushrooms, sliced
- 1 leek, chopped

Directions

1. Add chopped leek, garlic, celery and carrots to large soup pot. Simmer with 1/2 cup water until leeks are shiny and soft.
2. Dissolve miso in 4 cups water and add to pot.
3. Add potatoes, sliced mushrooms and beans. Add diced jalapeño or black pepper for less spice.
4. Cook until potatoes are tender. Add chopped greens of your choice.
5. Cook 5 minutes or until greens have softened. Serve and enjoy!

SERVINGS: 6

PER SERVING: Calories = 40; Total fat = 2g; Total carbohydrates = 10g; Protein = 8g; Sodium = 14mg; Fiber = 1.2g

Green Goddess Soup

Warm Me Up Chili

The reason there are chili cook-offs is that everyone has their own version. Ours is spicy, and we like to serve it over polenta. Cincinnati style is over pasta. Pick your beans, and have fun with different varieties.

Try chipotle pepper and smoked paprika for a more barbecue twist. Diced green peppers and onions make chili rich with flavor and antioxidants. Remember, cooked tomatoes have more lycopene than raw tomatoes. Lycopene is a powerful antioxidant with anti-cancer and cardiovascular protective properties.

One fact not often mentioned is lycopene's ability to protect the skin from aging and UV damage. Lycopene enhances production of anti-oxidative enzymes that protect the cells from harmful levels of reactive oxidative species clear singlet oxygen, which is a highly reactive molecule responsible for skin aging.

So enjoy the warmth this soup offers while it heals your body inside and out. This is a favorite for a cold night or perhaps a rainy day if you live in a southern climate as we do.

Ingredients

- 1 (15-ounce) can black beans
- 1 (15-ounce) can pinto beans
- 1 (15-ounce) can great northern beans
- 1 large (50-ounce) box chopped tomatoes
- 1 tablespoon tomato paste
- 1 medium red onion
- 1 jalapeño pepper
- 2 stalks celery
- 1 teaspoon chili powder
- 1 teaspoon garlic
- 1 teaspoon cumin
- 1/4 teaspoon cayenne pepper

Directions

1. Chop onion and celery fine and add to large saucepan.
2. Add beans, tomatoes, tomato paste and spices and bring to a boil. Let simmer for 1 hour. Alternatively, add Ingredients to an electric pressure cooker and set timer for 30 minutes.

Serve with a green salad and Cornbread Muffins (page 96), or add heartiness by serving over polenta or pasta.

SERVINGS: 6

PER SERVING: Calories = 212; Total fat = 1g; Total carbohydrates = 42g; Protein = 11g; Sodium = 60mg; Fiber = 14g

Warm Me Up Chili

Our Irish Eyes Are Smiling Potato Leek

My Grandma Addie's eyes are smiling, not only because my daughter is named after her, but because she has inherited her love for cooking.

Potato soup has always been a go-to meal in our family, and is considered a family comfort food. Potatoes grew well in my hometown, and each Labor Day my extended family of uncles, aunts and many of our neighbors would help harvest potatoes in each of their gardens. Hence, potatoes were a part of most dinners in the Dulaney household.

The russet potato is underestimated in nutrient density. It is packed with fiber, along with B vitamins and vitamin C. You can get 10% of the RDA in iron along with substantial amounts of magnesium and zinc from potatoes.

Leeks contain diallyl disulfide, which is converted to allicin. This compound inhibits HMG-CoA, thereby decreasing cholesterol. Allicin also has antibacterial and antiviral properties, making this soup a great go-to for an immunity booster. Leeks contain 55% of the RDA for vitamin A and 64ug of folate.

It is amazing that such a simple soup can be so incredibly packed with nutrients.

Ingredients

1 leek, diced
2 carrots, chopped
4 large potatoes
1 tablespoon miso
1 stalk celery, chopped
1 small bag frozen peas
1 cup plain, unsweetened almond milk
1 tablespoon nutritional yeast
Pepper to taste

Directions

1. Wash and chop leek, carrots and celery. Wash potatoes and cut into large pieces.
2. Sauté leek, carrots and celery with 1/4 cup of water on the sauté setting of your electric pressure cooker until slightly tender. (Note: lid will be off for this step.) Add frozen peas for a few minutes.
3. Add potatoes and remaining Ingredients to pressure cooker. Add enough water to cover the vegetables and create enough liquid for the soup. Secure the lid and set to soup function or 30 minutes on the timer.
4. Quick release the pressure cooker and remove the lid. Use an immersion blender to puree/blend the soup. If you do not have an immersion blender, you can pour contents of soup into a regular blender for the same effect.

SERVINGS: 6

PER SERVING: Calories = 159; Total fat = 1.1g; Total carbohydrates = 33g; Protein = 6.7g; Sodium = 302mg; Fiber = 7g

Our Irish Eyes Are Smiling Potato Leek

Must-go Vegetable Soup

When you clean out the refrigerator, everything must go; hence, we call this soup Must-go Vegetable. This soup can use up a lot of leftover and previously cooked vegetables.

You don't have to be vegan to like vegetable soup. We were having vegetable soup for dinner well before our plant-based life began. The only difference is that now, vegetables are used for the broth and the meat that used to "flavor" the soup is eliminated.

Vegetables provide plenty of flavor, and the soup is hearty and filling because of the potatoes and beans. Traditional vegetable soup has saturated fat, cholesterol and more sodium. This vegetable soup is loaded with fiber, antioxidants, and nitric oxide-producing vegetables.

Substitute your favorite bean or add additional varieties. Substitute kale or collards for cabbage, but remember to keep greens in the soup. If your family doesn't like greens, blend them in water before adding to the soup. They will not recognize the greens, but their taste buds will get to know the taste. Add bite-sized greens next, and soon enough, they will be eating greens.

Ingredients

- 3 large potatoes, diced
- 3 carrots, cubed
- 1 medium onion, diced
- 2 stalks celery, chopped
- 1 cup frozen corn
- 1 cup frozen peas
- 1 cup diced zucchini
- 2 boxes diced tomatoes
- 1 tablespoon hot pepper relish or one hot pepper

Directions

Add all Ingredients to an Instant Pot. Cover with 2 cups water and set the timer for 30 minutes.

SERVINGS: 6

PER SERVING: Calories = 195; Total fat = 1.3g; Total carbohydrates = 18g; Protein = 7g; Sodium = 118mg; Fiber = 9g

Must-go Vegetable Soup

Miso Immune Booster Soup

This is my version of a healing soup that feels good all the way down. Loaded with antioxidants and phytonutrients, this soup will get you feeling better quickly. It can be made more calorie-dense by adding cubed tofu or rice. The roasted onion and garlic give an added depth of flavor. Leeks can be substituted for onions.

The roasted onion and garlic give an added depth of flavor. I make this soup in the electric pressure cooker on the sauté mode. This soup would be a great afternoon pick-me-up and better for you than any energy drink or potion.

Ingredients

- 2 tablespoons miso
- 1 bulb garlic
- 1 medium onion
- 4 cups finely chopped mushrooms (your choice of variety, but I recommend shitake for at least 1 cup)
- 4 scallions, chopped fine

Directions

1. Fill a medium saucepan ¾ of the way with water. Add miso and simmer.
2. Cut off the top of the garlic bulb and checkerboard-dice an onion.
3. Roast the onion and garlic bulb at 400°F for 15 minutes.
4. Add 3 cups chopped mushrooms to the saucepan.
5. Add onion and roasted garlic cloves to the saucepan and bring to a boil for 15 minutes
6. Reduce heat to medium and simmer. Using an immersion blender, blend soup to a fine purée.
7. Add the remaining cup of sliced mushrooms to soup and simmer for 15 minutes.
8. Top with chopped scallions and serve.

SERVINGS: 6

PER SERVING: Calories = 396; Total fat = 2g; Total carbohydrates = 68g; Protein = 26g; Sodium = 274mg; Fiber = 29g; Iron = 34%

Miso Immune Booster Soup

Fifteen Bean Veggie Supreme

Bean soup is best with a variety of beans. Most grocery stores sell a bag of mixed dried beans for next to nothing. Soaking beans releases natural surfactants and activates enzymes in the beans that make them more digestible. By starting off sautéing carrots, celery, and onions to generate a good broth, and then adding the soaked beans, you are making this a hearty, nutrient-dense meal. Adding elbow macaroni and potatoes makes it more calorie-dense.

Ingredients

1 package 15 bean soup mix (can be purchased on Amazon or in most grocery stores). Alternatively, mix 2 cups of your favorite dried beans and lentils.
4 cups kale, chopped (or frozen chopped kale)
3 large carrots, chopped
2 medium zucchini, diced
1 red onion, chopped fine
4 stalks celery, chopped
1 large package white mushrooms, chopped
1 tablespoon minced garlic

Directions

1. Soak beans overnight. (Alternatively, place the rinsed dried beans in an electric pressure cooker, cover with water 1 inch above the beans and bring the pot to pressure. Release, and rinse beans. Cover beans again and set timer on pressure cooker for 40 minutes.)
2. While your beans are cooking, in a separate pot sauté onion, carrots and garlic in water.
3. Once softened, add celery, zucchini, mushrooms and kale.
4. Add more water to create a broth and simmer until beans have finished cooking.
5. Once beans are done, add cooked vegetables and broth to the pot.
6. Add the seasoning packet. If you would like a smokier flavor, add smoked paprika. You can also add cayenne pepper, black pepper and Sriracha to taste.
7. If the soup is still too thick, add water and let simmer in pressure cooker on warm setting.

SERVINGS: 6

PER SERVING: Calories = 396; Total fat = 2g; Total carbohydrates = 68g; Protein = 26g; Sodium = 274mg; Fiber = 29g; Iron = 34%

Fifteen Bean Veggie Supreme

Immune-boosting Broccoli

Broccoli is a nutritional powerhouse containing loads of antioxidants, vitamin C, and fiber and is a nitric oxide-booster as well. If you are having trouble getting in those 5 cups of greens, look no further than this soup.

Cooking broccoli well makes it easier to digest, and using a hand blender makes it very creamy. The starch in the potato along with the nutritional yeast gives this a cheesy taste and feel. This soup will protect and nourish the whole family and is a great way to introduce children to broccoli.

We like this soup served with a grilled vegetable sandwich such as zucchini, tomato, onion and avocado on whole-wheat toast.

Ingredients

1 large head broccoli
1 medium potato
1 cup nut milk
1/4 cup nutritional yeast
1 tablespoon light miso paste
2 carrots
1 leek
4 cloves garlic, diced
1 teaspoon turmeric
1/4 teaspoon black pepper

Directions for electric pressure cooker

1. Chop broccoli into florets, peel the stem and add to the cooking pot.
2. Chop carrots and leeks and add to the pot.
3. Add nut milk and enough water to just cover the vegetables.
4. Add miso, garlic and dry spices.
5. Cover and set pressure cooker to 15 minutes.
6. Quick release the pressure when done.
7. Use an immersion blender to blend vegetables until creamy.
8. Add pepper to taste and serve.

SERVINGS: 6

PER SERVING: Calories = 68; Total fat = 1g; Total carbohydrates = 12g; Protein = 5g; Sodium = 73mg; Fiber = 3g; Iron = 8%

Immune-boosting Broccoli

Spicy Black Bean Fiesta

This soup has become not only a family favorite, but a nutrition class favorite as well. Refreshing flavors from cilantro and lime juice combined with the spicy kick from salsa, jalapeño pepper and spices provide a flavorful experience with every bite!

We cannot forget to mention the nutrients packed in to this soup — nitric oxide-producing kale, antioxidant-rich bell peppers, garlic and mushrooms, plus the iron- and protein-rich black beans. Wow your friends with this delicious and nutrient-dense dish that can be eaten alone, paired with a baked potato, or poured over a whole grain of your choice.

Ingredients

1 onion, chopped fine
3 cloves garlic, minced
2 red or orange bell peppers, diced
1/2 jalapeño pepper, diced
2 cups kale, chopped fine (alternatively, use S blade in a food processor)
1 large box white mushrooms, chopped fine (or use S blade in a food processor)
1-1/2 teaspoons cumin
2 tablespoons chili powder
1-1/2 cups fresh salsa
2 cans (15-ounces each) organic, low-sodium black beans (or cook from dry beans)
1 can (28-ounce) organic, low-sodium crushed tomatoes
1 can (14.5-ounce) organic, low-sodium diced tomatoes
1 package (14.4-ounce) frozen corn

Directions

1. In a large soup pot, sauté onion, garlic and peppers in water until soft. Add 1-1/2 cups of water and bring to a simmer.
2. Add chopped kale. When kale is soft, add salsa, tomatoes and spices.
3. Add rinsed black beans and corn. Add 1 cup of water to thin soup, if needed.
4. Simmer, stirring occasionally.
5. Reduce heat, cover and let cook for about 30 minutes. Flavors increase over time, making the soup even better the next day.
6. Add optional toppings before serving.

Optional garnishes for serving: lime juice, fresh cilantro, red onion and avocado. To reduce spice, choose a mild salsa and omit jalapeño pepper.

SERVINGS: 6

PER SERVING: Calories = 302; Total fat = 1g; Total carbohydrates = 58g; Protein = 14g; Sodium = 392mg; Fiber = 14g; Iron = 21%

Spicy Black Bean Fiesta

Carrot Ginger Soup with a Protein Punch

This is an anti-inflammatory, immune-boosting superstar. Carrots are loaded with beta carotene, giving them loads of anti-cancer properties. Ginger is an immune booster and gives this soup a kick. You can make this savory by boosting the paprika and cumin or make it very smooth with more garam masala and cinnamon.

Ingredients

5 large carrots, chopped into large pieces
1 medium yellow onion, chopped fine
2 medium potatoes, peeled and diced
2 gloves garlic, minced
1-1/2 inch knob fresh ginger root, peeled and grated
1 teaspoon cumin
1 teaspoon garam masala
1 teaspoon paprika
1-1/2 cups lentils, rinsed
2 tablespoons lemon juice
Pepper to taste

Directions

1. Add chopped carrots, onion, potatoes, garlic and ginger to an electric pressure cooker or large saucepan.
2. Add rinsed lentils. Cover with water, and secure lid and select soup setting for electric pressure cooker. If cooking on top of stove, bring to a boil and then reduce to medium heat and simmer for 1 hour.
3. Once cooked, add lemon juice and use immersion blender to completely blend all Ingredients.
4. Add more water if needed to thin soup.
5. Add additional spices to taste, then mix and serve.

SERVINGS: 6

PER SERVING: Calories = 154; Total fat = 0g; Total carbohydrates = 37g; Protein = 12g; Sodium = 74mg; Fiber = 14g; Iron = 25%

Carrot Ginger Soup with a Protein Punch

Tomato Basil Blast Soup

Canned tomato soup was one of my favorite lunches growing up. Canned soups are very high in sodium, and I increased that by adding salty crackers. Homemade tomato soup tastes so much better and is much more nutritious. Tomatoes are rich in antioxidants. The vitamin C in tomatoes varies with the color and ripeness. Sundried tomatoes have the highest content with 39 mg/100grams compared with orange tomatoes containing 16mg/100grams.

Tomatoes also contain carotenoids such as lutein, lycopene, and beta carotene. These help decrease inflammation and also have been shown to decrease the effects of excessive UV radiation from sunlight.

Tomatoes are also a good source of B vitamins, magnesium, zinc and vitamin E. They increase heart health by decreasing platelet stickiness, thereby decreasing blood clot formation. Tomatoes have been shown to decrease cholesterol, LDL and triglycerides as well as decreasing the accumulation of cholesterol in macrophages. Together, these mechanisms can decrease atherosclerotic changes in the blood vessels.

Lycopene is an antioxidant associated with anti-cancer properties effective against breast and prostate cancers. Another key nutrient is alpha-tomatine, which has been shown to decrease cell growth in prostate cancers.

With all of these benefits in mind, feel free to have another bowl of tomato soup and add tomatoes to your salad!

Ingredients

6 medium tomatoes, chopped
1 box (25-ounce) chopped tomatoes
2 stalks celery
1 medium sweet yellow onion
1/2 cup fresh basil
4 cloves garlic
1 teaspoon of yellow miso
1/2 teaspoon black pepper
1 jalapeño pepper (or green pepper to limit spiciness)

Directions

1. Finely chop celery and onion and add to a saucepan.
2. Dice garlic and add to pan.
3. Add miso and 1/2 cup of water.
4. Sautée until onions are translucent.
5. Add box of tomatoes to the saucepan.
6. In a blender, add fresh tomatoes and pepper and blend until smooth.
7. Add the mixture to the saucepan, with black pepper
8. Chop basil coarsely and add to saucepan. (Reserve some basil for garnish.)
9. Bring the soup to a boil then simmer 30 minutes
10. Garnish with basil and serve.

SERVINGS: 6

PER SERVING: Calories = 68; Total fat = 0g; Total carbohydrates = 12g; Protein = 3g; Sodium = 85mg; Fiber = 5g; Iron = 6%

Tomato Basil Blast Soup

Chapter 9:

Desserts that Heal

Something sweet after meals and even for breakfast has been a favorite in the Dulaney household. I grew up around beautiful pies and cakes. In fact, most of the fruit I ate growing up was in a pie. With this also came too many calories, too much sugar and fat, along with the development of an intense craving for sweets. The brakes had to be applied.

Portion control with sweets and treats is very difficult for most people. It starts out OK, but it doesn't take long before it is an everyday, every meal, excessive portion ritual. Sweets and treats are constantly seen on TV and social media. Sweet treats are rewards for good behavior, both in school and in the workplace. For some people, sugar addiction is not easy to control, and it leads to mindless eating.

These dessert recipes are conservative with regard to simple sugars and fats, but they are calorie-dense and should be portion-controlled and not an everyday food.

On the bright side, many of the recipes contain vegetables, beans, and fruit, so they provide a good source of many nutrients despite being calorie-dense.

Chickpea Chocolate Chip Cookies

When you think of cookies, you are most likely not thinking of your health. However, we believe that these two trains of thought do not need to be mutually exclusive. With a base of chickpeas, your cookie now contains plant-strong protein and fiber. By using peanut butter powder, you get the taste of peanuts without the high amounts of oil. Combined with minimal natural sweetener used and wholesome dairy-free dark chocolate, you can enjoy a sweet treat with nutritional purpose in mind.

Ingredients

- 1-1/2 cups chickpeas, drained and rinsed
- 1/4 cup natural almond butter
- 1 tablespoon peanut butter powder
- 1/4 cup maple syrup
- 3 tablespoons dairy-free chocolate chips
- 2 teaspoons baking soda
- 1 teaspoon vanilla extract

Directions

1. Preheat oven to 350° F and line a baking sheet with parchment paper.
2. If using canned chickpeas, rinse well. If cooking from dry beans, make sure cooked beans are drained and cooled completely before making cookies.
3. Blend all Ingredients in a food processor until a smooth batter forms.
4. If consistency is too thick, add a small amount of water or plain plant milk to thin.
5. Scoop out dough with a spoon, and roll into balls, then place on baking sheet
6. Bake for 10-12 minutes, or until cookies are slightly brown.
   Note: These cookies will be soft; allow to cool completely before serving.
7. Store in an airtight container in the refrigerator.

SERVINGS: about 10

PER SERVING: Calories = 129; Total fat = 6g; Total carbohydrates = 17g; Protein = 4g; Sodium = 306mg; Fiber = 3g; Iron = 6%

Chickpea Chocolate Chip Cookies

Black Bean Brownie Bites

While black beans are more commonly seen as an ingredient in savory plant-based dishes, their role in these brownie bites is amazing, to say the least! Black beans are an excellent source of healthful minerals such as iron and calcium, as well as fantastic sources of plant-based protein and fiber. The flavor of the black beans is hidden by the natural cacao powder while providing a smooth and moist base to these brownies.

Ingredients

1 can (15-ounce) black beans, rinsed and drained
3 large flaxseed eggs (3 tablespoon ground flaxseed meal plus 9 tablespoons water)
¾ cup cacao powder
1/4 teaspoon sea salt
1 teaspoon pure vanilla extract
1/2 cup chopped dates (about 6 large dates)
1-1/2 teaspoons baking powder
Optional toppings: crushed walnuts, pecans, or semi-sweet dairy-free chocolate chips

Directions

1. Preheat oven to 350°F.
2. Line a muffin pan with parchment paper (line cake pan if making larger brownie).
3. Prepare flaxseed eggs by combining the ground flaxseed and water in the bowl of the food processor. Pulse to combine and then let rest for a few minutes to thicken.
4. Add remaining Ingredients to the food processor bowl (minus optional toppings) and purée for about 3 minutes, scraping down sides as needed, until smooth.
5. If the batter appears too thick, add a tablespoon of water at a time and pulse again. The batter should be thinner than frosting, but not runny.
6. Pour batter evenly into muffin cups or cake pan, and smooth the top with a spoon.
7. Sprinkle with optional toppings.
8. Bake 20-26 minutes or until the tops are dry and edges start to pull away from the sides (typically 25 minutes).
9. Remove from oven and let cool 30 minutes before removing brownies from pan. They will be tender, so remove gently with a fork. The insides are meant to be very fudgy, so don't be concerned if they seem too moist.
10. Store in an airtight container in the refrigerator.

SERVINGS: 12

PER SERVING: Calories = 81; Total fat = 1g; Total carbohydrates = 16g; Protein = 3g; Sodium = 85mg; Fiber = 3g; Iron = 4%

Black Bean Brownie Bites

Banana Bread

It is banana and bread. How could that derail your plant-based nutrition? If it's bought from a coffee shop or bakery, you can be sure it will. Traditional banana breads and coffee cakes have oil and plenty of sugar. Some may even have eggs. Here is a healthy alternative you can share at the office that everyone will enjoy.

Ingredients

4 ripe bananas, mashed
2 flax eggs (2 tablespoon ground flaxseed
   plus 6 tablespoon water)
1/3 cup maple syrup
1/3 cup unsweetened almond milk
1 tablespoon vanilla extract
1/4 cup molasses
1/2 cup oats
1-1/2 cups whole-wheat flour (or GF all-purpose flour)
1 teaspoon baking soda
1 teaspoon baking powder
2 teaspoons cinnamon
1/2 cup chopped walnuts

Directions

1. Preheat oven to 350°F.
2. Make "flax eggs" and set aside to thicken.
3. Combine wet Ingredients in a mixing bowl and add in flax egg mixture.
4. Combine dry Ingredients in a large mixing bowl and fold in wet Ingredients, mixing thoroughly.
5. Pour batter into a greased bread pan and bake 45-55 minutes or until golden brown (50 minutes recommended).

SERVINGS: 10

PER SERVING: Calories = 227; Total fat = 6g; Total carbohydrates = 42g; Protein = 5g; Sodium = 144mg; Fiber = 5g; Iron = 9%

Banana Bread

Carrot Cake Muffins

This is one of my favorite desserts, and I smile thinking of how appalled I was when an aunt served carrot cake for my cousin's first birthday. At that point in my life, only chocolate cake was acceptable for a birthday.

Today, I love the spices in carrot cake. These muffins are sweetened with pineapple and dried fruit, providing nutrients and fiber along with natural sugars.

Ingredients

4 flax eggs (4 tablespoon ground flaxseed plus 8 tablespoons warm water)
1/4 cup pure maple syrup
1 cup unsweetened applesauce
1 can (20-ounce) organic, natural crushed pineapple in natural juice, drained (or fresh pineapple)
1/2 teaspoon salt
1-1/2 teaspoons baking soda
1-1/2 teaspoons baking powder
2 teaspoons ground cinnamon
1 teaspoon ginger
1 cup plain, unsweetened plant-based milk
2 teaspoons vanilla extract
2 cups loosely packed grated carrots
2-1/2 cups whole wheat flour
Optional Ingredients: 1/2 cup chopped walnuts and/or 1/2 cup raisins

Directions

1. Preheat oven to 350°F and line muffin tins with parchment.
2. Prepare flax eggs in a small bowl and set aside to thicken.
3. Chop carrots and pineapple (separately) in a food processor and set aside.
4. In a large mixing bowl, combine dry Ingredients, blending well.
5. In a medium-sized mixing bowl, combine maple syrup, applesauce, pineapple, milk and vanilla.
6. Add wet Ingredients to dry Ingredients, mixing well.
7. Fold in grated carrots and optional Ingredients (walnuts and/or raisins).
8. Pour evenly into muffin tins.
9. Bake 30-35 minutes, testing with a toothpick to check when done.
10. Remove from oven and place on a cooling rack to cool before serving.

SERVINGS: 22

PER SERVING: Calories = 77; Total fat = 1g; Total carbohydrates = 16g; Protein = 2g; Sodium = 159mg; Fiber = 2g; Iron = 3%

Carrot Cake Muffins

Lemon Poppy Seed Blueberry Muffins

My Noonie and I love all things citrus. Growing up, my mom would tease me when I chose fruity treats over chocolate — how the tables have turned! She has seen a big change in cravings and taste buds since we became plant-based as a family, and now prefers whole fruits to traditional desserts.

Friends and clients often ask me for muffin recipes. These lemon poppy seed muffins are always a recommendation. You can add more fresh or frozen blueberries for more flavor. This mildly sweet citrus treat is perfect to take to work gatherings, school functions and brunches.

Ingredients

2 chia eggs (2 tablespoons chia seeds plus 6 tablespoons warm water)
1 cup unsweetened applesauce
1/3 cup lemon juice
1 tablespoon lemon extract
2 heaping tablespoons lemon zest
1 teaspoon vanilla
1/4 cup almond milk
1/3 cup maple syrup
1-1/2 teaspoons baking soda
1 tablespoon poppy seeds (optional)
1/2 cup rolled oats
1-1/2 cups whole wheat pastry flour (or substitute unbleached all-purpose or GF all-purpose blend)
1-1/2 cups blueberries (fresh or frozen — note that frozen may turn the batter purple)

Directions

1. Preheat oven to 375°F. Line muffin tins with parchment.
2. Prepare chia seed eggs, setting aside to congeal.
3. Combine applesauce, lemon juice, lemon extract, vanilla, almond milk and maple syrup in a medium-sized mixing bowl.
4. In a large mixing bowl, combine baking soda, rolled oats and flour.
5. Add wet Ingredients to dry Ingredients then add blueberries, mixing well.
6. Bake 20-25 minutes.
7. Let cool and serve.
8. Muffins can be stored in an airtight container for 5 days.

SERVINGS: 12

PER SERVING: Calories = 118; Total fat = 1g; Total carbohydrates = 26g; Protein = 3g; Sodium = 162mg; Fiber = 5g; Iron = 6%

Lemon Poppy Seed Blueberry Muffins

Lime Pie

This is one of our most calorie-dense recipes. Traditional crusts have a lot of fat, and nut crusts are no exception. By making a crust ahead of time using this granola-derived recipe you can cut the fat and calories. I prefer Florida avocados for desserts because of their increased water content and lower fiber content, which makes the fillings much smoother and creamier. Limes and berries contain antioxidants and phytonutrients, adding a healthy twist over traditional pies. There is also significant fiber in this dessert from the fruit, oats and dates.

Ingredients

Crust

1 cup walnuts
1 cup oats
1 cup unsweetened coconut
6 Medjool dates
1 teaspoon vanilla
2 tablespoons lime juice

Filling

2 ripe avocados
1 box silken tofu
2 tablespoons lime zest
4 tablespoons lime juice
3 tablespoons maple syrup
1/2 teaspoon vanilla extract
1 cup fresh berries (blackberries, raspberries or strawberries)

Directions

Crust

1. Place Ingredients a food processor and blend using the S blade until dough forms.
2. Transfer contents to a pie pan and press down to form a pie shell.
3. Place shell in the freezer while making the filling.

Filling

1. Add filling Ingredients to food processor and, using the S blade, blend until creamy.
2. Transfer to the pie crust and refrigerate until ready to serve.
3. Top with fresh berries as garnish

CRUST - SERVINGS: 8

PER SERVING: Calories = 227; Total fat = 14g; Total carbohydrates = 24g; Protein = 5g; Sodium = 1mg; Fiber = 4g; Iron = 6%

FILLING - SERVINGS: 8

PER SERVING: Calories = 116; Total fat = 7g; Total carbohydrates = 12g; Protein = 5g; Sodium = 4mg; Fiber = 3g; Iron = 4%

Lime Pie

Pumpkin Pie

One of our favorite things about fall is pumpkin. It is versatile, tasty and so full of nutrients. My grandmother grew butternut squash and used them exclusively in her pumpkin pies and cookies. I believe there was a pumpkin pie on the table from August through January. Traditional pie crusts are made out of solidified oils and white flour. Hers were made with lard, making them very high in saturated fat. Our crusts now provide essential nutrients that enhance the flavor of the filling as well as your health!

Ingredients

Crust
4 dates
1/4 cup pecans
1/4 cup walnuts
1/4 cup rolled oats

Filling
1-1/2 cans pumpkin puree
1/4 cup maple syrup
4 chopped dates
1/3 cup almond milk
1 box silken tofu
1 teaspoon cinnamon
1/4 teaspoon ground cloves
1/4 teaspoon allspice
1/4 teaspoon nutmeg

Directions

Crust
1. Add Ingredients to a food processor and mix with the S blade until a dough ball forms.
2. Transfer to a pie plate and press to form a crust. Set aside.

Filling
1. Place all Ingredients into the food processor and, using the S blade, blend until smooth.
2. Transfer to the pie crust and bake 50-60 minutes at 350°F or until the filling begins to crack.

CRUST - SERVINGS: 6

PER SERVING: Calories = 122; Total fat = 7g; Total carbohydrates = 16g; Protein = 2g; Sodium = 0mg; Fiber = 2g; Iron = 3%

FILLING - SERVINGS: 8

PER SERVING: Calories = 172; Total fat = 3g; Total carbohydrates = 34g; Protein = 6g; Sodium = 11mg; Fiber = 2g; Iron = 9%

Pumpkin Pie

Ice Cream

Ice cream is one of my favorite desserts of all time, and probably what I thought I would miss most when I became vegan. The early commercial soy versions seemed to be chemistry experiments with a lot of sugar and an aftertaste. The taste has improved with commercial non-dairy ice creams at the expense of a lot of sugar and fat. I have found I enjoy a cold, fruity dessert rather than a fatty dessert. Who knew bananas could be so versatile?

I use bananas as a base to make ice cream and add other fruits and spices depending on my mood.

Some of my favorites are cherry-chocolate, piña colada, eggless nog, mango and blueberry chocolate.

Ingredients
   2 frozen bananas
   2 cups of frozen fruit of your choice

Cherry Chocolate or Blueberry Chocolate
   2 tablespoons of cacao powder
   1 cup frozen cherries or blueberries

Piña Colada
   1 cup pineapple
   1 tablespoon dried coconut

Eggless Nog
   1 teaspoon cinnamon
   1/4 teaspoon nutmeg
   1 teaspoon turmeric
   1 teaspoon ginger

Directions
1. Pulse bananas on low in a high-speed blender then up the power as the fruit spins. Use the tamper to keep the mixture blending until creamy.
2. Garnish with berries or cacao nibs if desired.

Nutritional information will vary depending on fruits chosen and serving sizes.

Ice Cream

Blueberry Mango Crumble

Mangoes and blueberries are two of my favorite fruits. There is no overdosing on the benefits of blueberries, as they are loaded with brain-powering antioxidants. Mangoes are rich in vitamin C and beta-carotenoids. This is a quick, healthy dessert that the whole family will enjoy. Serve warm or cold.

Substitute other seasonable fruits or those locally available to give this dessert a new twist. Frozen fruit is also a great option if your favorite fruit is out of season.

Ingredients

- 2 cups fresh or frozen blueberries
- 1 cup chopped fresh or frozen mango
- 1 cup oats
- 1/2 cup nut milk
- 1/4 cup walnuts, chopped
- 1 teaspoon cinnamon
- 1/2 teaspoon ginger
- 1/4 teaspoon ground cloves

Directions

1. Preheat oven to 350°F.
2. Arrange blueberries and mangoes in the bottom of an 8 x 8 glass dish.
3. In a separate bowl, mix oats and nut milk. Add cinnamon, ginger and cloves. Mix well.
4. Pour oat mixture over fruit and top with chopped walnuts.
5. Sprinkle with cinnamon and bake 20 minutes or until oats appear slightly crisp.

SERVINGS: 6

PER SERVING: Calories = 136; Total fat = 5g; Total carbohydrates = 22g; Protein = 3g; Sodium = 15mg; Fiber = 4g; Iron = 6%

Blueberry Mango Crumble

Toasted Coconut Banana Cream Pudding

This dessert is a cross between vegan crème brûlée and pudding. It's a good example of how desserts can be sweet and healthy. Because we are blending ingredients, we are creating a calorie-dense dessert that is also nutrient-dense. Stick to the portion size listed below and enjoy on a special occasion.

Ingredients

1 box firm tofu
4 ripe bananas
1/4 cup soaked cashews
1/2 cup unsweetened coconut or almond milk
2 teaspoons vanilla
2 tablespoons ground chia seeds
2 tablespoons maple syrup
1 tablespoon unsweetened coconut, toasted

Directions

1. Place cashews, chia seeds and nut milk in the blender or food processor and blend until smooth.
2. Add bananas and tofu and continue to blend.
3. Add vanilla and maple syrup.
4. Line individual ramekins with thinly sliced bananas.
5. Add the pudding mixture and top with the toasted coconut.
6. Refrigerate an hour before serving.

SERVINGS: 6

PER SERVING: Calories = 177; Total Fat = 4g; Total Carbohydrates = 27g; Protein = 7g; Sodium = 30mg; Fiber = 4g; Iron = 7%

Toasted Coconut Banana Cream Pudding

About The Authors

Jami Dulaney, MD

Jami Dulaney knew she wanted to be a physician at a very young age. She was frequently in the back seat when her parents drove her grandmother to the hospital to be admitted for congestive heart failure and diabetic ketoacidosis.

Her grandparents died of diabetes and heart disease much too young.

Consequently, she attended medical school at West Virginia University and earned a residency and fellowship at the University of Pittsburgh in internal medicine and cardiology.

Dr. Dulaney spent over 15 years in a traditional medical practice, adhering to the guidelines for treatment set by the American College of Cardiology and American College of Internal Medicine. The goal was to manage lifestyle diseases by adjusting medications and performing procedures to keep the patient functioning at the highest possible level. Medications were added, but never taken away, and patients were monitored with testing to detect early disease progression.

Trying to avoid her family history of diabetes and heart disease, Dr. Dulaney began running marathons. Although she became fit, her lipid profile was not stellar, by any means. After reading the book, "A Diet for a New America" by John Robbins, she became vegan. After watching the documentary, "Forks over Knives," she decided to add plant-based nutrition education to her medical practice.

Then something miraculous happened. Her patients began making dramatic improvements in their diabetes, cholesterol readings, blood pressure, angina, and even their neuropathies. By changing their diet, they became symptom-free and were able to eliminate many medications even after many years of suffering with lifestyle diseases.

Dr. Dulaney added more nutrition classes, and in 2017, completely changed her practice to focus on the reversal of lifestyle diseases through plant-based nutrition.

She believes every medical practice should have a registered dietitian on staff, and was excited to be joined by her daughter, Addie Dulaney Majnaric, RDN. Together, they are teaching and counseling their members on the benefits of a plant-based lifestyle. Her mother, Alfreda Dulaney, joined her locally to help with the nutrition classes and together, the three Dulaney ladies began to develop recipes and meal plans that the members could enjoy while becoming healthy.

Dr. Dulaney loves to create colorful dishes that incorporate greens, grains and vegetables that are pleasing to the eye and the palate. She is still running marathons and improving her speed. She has added ultra-marathons and Ironman triathlons to her list of accomplishments and hopes to continue enjoying these events well into an advanced age.

What a strange turn of events to trade a heart catheter for a spatula. It is fitting that a strong family history of heart disease and lifestyle disease led to the practice of medicine, and a family love of cooking led to the ultimate treatment and cure of many of the lifestyle diseases that plague so many.

Addie Dulaney Majnaric, RDN, LD

What number truly qualifies as too many cooks in the kitchen? In terms of the Dulaney ladies, we hit maximum capacity with the addition of Addie Dulaney Majnaric, daughter of Jami and granddaughter of Alfreda.

Named after Dr. Dulaney's own grandmother, who was an incredible cook, and growing up in a tight-knit family of cooks, it comes as no surprise that Addie inherited and developed an affinity for cooking and baking.

A native of her family's home-grown area of "Almost Heaven," West Virginia, Addie grew up mostly in sunny southwest Florida with her mom, Jami, and just a few streets over from her "Noonie and Pappy," Alfreda and Jim Dulaney. Most would describe Addie as a mix of the two women before her: a spunky, funny Italian gal like Alfreda, with strong roots, a love for helping people, and an obsession for distance running like her mom, Jami.

Addie grew up in her mother's medical practice — greeting patients at the office and tagging along with her mom on rounds at the local hospitals — and was no stranger to the work her mother did. From a young age, she knew she wanted to help people, just as she had seen her mother do. After examining different avenues of health care, Addie became drawn to nutrition when her family transitioned to a plant-based diet, shortly after her Noonie was diagnosed with lymphoma. She was able to see first-hand the importance of nutrition in disease reversal and how it can help others prevent common lifestyle diseases.

Addie graduated with honors from West Virginia University, with a bachelor of science in exercise physiology, a bachelor of science in human nutrition and foods, and a minor in strength and conditioning.

She was a Division I athlete on the women's varsity rowing team, and also saw a change in her personal health when she transitioned completely to a plant-based diet. She experienced gains in athletic performance and developed a healthier relationship with food. The choice was clear: dietetics and wellness were her destiny. After completing graduate courses, a yearlong dietetic internship, and passing her licensure exam, Addie became a registered dietitian nutritionist.

Addie now serves as the registered dietitian on staff at Dr. Dulaney's practice. She consults with members of the practice locally, and leads nutrition coaching calls with patients from afar. She contributes to nutrition class curriculum, composes all practice newsletters and membership web-based content. She loves creating monthly wellness challenges for the members, seeing her clients become empowered through nutrition education, and getting to work every day alongside her mentor and inspiration, her mom, Jami Dulaney.

Alfreda Cecelia Dulaney

Alfreda Cecelia Dulaney was born Alfreda Cecelia Guidi in a small town in western Pennsylvania and moved to West Virginia at a young age. As in most Italian households, her mother was the matriarch of the kitchen. As a child, she was the assistant, making ravioli by dropping in the filling and using a fork to close the dough. Pasta and meat sauce were staples, as well as meat dishes and greens from the garden.

Alfreda credits her Irish mother-in-law, Addie, for teaching her to cook. Hers was a much different style, revolving around fried foods with meat, garden vegetables, and homemade bread at each meal. Over the years, she combined her love of Italian food with her proficiency in cooking Irish food to develop her own style of cooking.

Working full time as a bookkeeper and then cooking dinner each evening, she used organization and planning skills to get high-quality, made-from-scratch meals on the table to feed her family. There was a side salad most nights along with meat, a potato and a vegetable. The meat was raised on one of the family's farms and most of the vegetables came from the backyard garden.

As the years progressed, she began to develop the lifestyle diseases of her family, including high cholesterol, diabetes and hypertension. She also suffered from gastroesophageal reflux as her father had, and she assumed all of these conditions were hereditary.

It was not until she developed lymphoma that Alfreda adopted a plant-based diet and attributed her successful course of chemotherapy and remission to the support offered by plant-based nutrition. She found giving up salt was easier if she added other spices to her diet. She was pleasantly surprised when her longstanding history of reflux disappeared, allowing her to stop her medications. Gradually, she started revamping her recipes to be plant-based, without added salt or oil.

Alfreda has been an invaluable asset in the nutrition classes at her daughter's medical practice. Her bubbly personality and witty humor makes everyone feel at home. She offers input into the recipes and is a mentor for those beginning their plant-based journey. At 86, she is still golfing and participating in Zumba and yoga classes

Her pasta sauce and stuffed shells are her signature dishes that everyone wants on special occasions. She is the creator of many of the soups in this book and for the nutrition classes that you will surely enjoy.

Becoming plant-based has opened up a whole new chapter for good health, improved energy, and memorable times with her daughter and granddaughter.

Shopping Lists

Pantry List

Beans & Canned Goods	Whole Grains	Flours	Baking Supplies	Miscellaneous
Black beans	Old-fashioned oats	Whole wheat flour	Dates	Nutritional yeast Spices
Pinto beans	Rice	Cornmeal	Applesauce	Balsamic vinegar
Garbanzo beans	Quinoa	Corn flour	Vanilla	Rice vinegar
Great northern beans	Couscous	Tapioca flour	Baking soda	Walnuts
Navy beans	Barley	Cornstarch	Baking powder	Flaxseed
Butter beans	Whole wheat pasta	Teff flour	Apple cider vinegar	Chia seeds
Kidney beans	Lentil pasta	GF all-purpose flour	Vegan chocolate chips	Hemp hearts
Lentils	Bulgur wheat		Raisins	Yeast
Soy curls				Silken tofu
Artichokes				Mustard
Diced tomatoes				BBQ sauce
Crushed tomatoes				Ketchup
Plain tomato sauce				
Hot pepper relish				

Shopping Lists

Weekly Perishables				
Greens	**Vegetables**	**Fruit**	**Plant Milks**	**Refrigerated Protein Sources**
Spinach	Mushrooms	Tomatoes	Almond	Tofu
Kale	Peppers	Avocados	Soy	Tempeh
Cabbage	Onion	Lemons	Cashew	
Bok choy	Garlic	Limes	Rice	
Brussels sprouts	Broccoli	Bananas	Coconut	
Swiss chard	White potatoes	Melons		
Collard greens	Sweet potatoes	Blueberries		
Beet tops	Beets	Peaches		
Parsley	Cucumber	Apples		
	Carrots	Kiwi		
	Zucchini	Oranges		
	Eggplant	Pineapple		
	Celery	Mango		
	Squash	Strawberries		
	Peas	Other berries		
	Okra			
	Cauliflower			

Conversion Charts

1 ounce = 2 tablespoons

1 pint = 2 cups

¾ cup = 6 ounces

1/4 cup = 2 ounces

1/8 cup = 1 ounce

8 ounces = 1 cup

1/2 cup is 4 ounces = 8 table-

spoons

8 x 8 x 2 pan = 8 cups

7 x 11 x 2 pan = 6 cups

9 x 13 pan = 14 cups

9 x 5 inch loaf pan = 8 cups

350 degrees = 180 Celsius

400 degrees = 200 Celsius

200 degrees = 93 Celsius

One pound = 16 ounces

One liter = 34 ounces

8 ounces = 227 grams

12 ounces = 340 grams

1 pound = 454 grams

Kitchen Hacks by the Dulaney Ladies

- Use old credit cards or plastic hotel keys as pot scrubbers for baked-on food.

- Dip bananas or apple slices in lemon juice to keep from browning.

- Soak potatoes in cold water for an hour before baking to add crispness.

- Prepare a marinade of fresh herbs and balsamic vinegar in the blender and use for roasting vegetables instead of oil.

- Buy fruit on sale, then chop and freeze for smoothies and sorbets.

Nutrition Facts

* The Percent Daily Values are based on a 2,000 calorie diet, so your values may change depending on your calorie needs. The values here may not be 100% accurate because the recipes have not been professionally evaluated nor have they been evaluated by the U.S. FDA.

References

Prevent and Reverse Heart Disease: The Revolutionary, Scientifically Proven, Nutrition Based Cure. Caldwell B. Esselstyn Jr., M.D.

Gabriela Gutierrez-Salmean, Theodore P. et al. Effects of (-)-epicatechin on moleculular modulators of skeletal muscle growth and differentiation. J Nutr Biochem. 2014 Jan;25(1):10.1016.

Potter GA, Burke MD. Salvestrols-natural products with tumour selective activity. Journal of Orthomol. Medicine 2006;21(1):34-36.

Gagan BN Chainy, Sunil K Manna, Madan M Chaturvedi and Bharat B Aggarwal. Anethole blocks both early and late cellular responses transduced by tumor necrosis factor: effect on NF-kB, AP-1, JNK, MapKK and apoptosis. Concogen 19, 2943-2950 (June 08, 2008).

LI PG et al Anticancer effects of sweet potato protein on human colorectal cancer cells. World J Gastroenterol. 2013 Jun7;19(21):3300-8

J Kobayashi, T Yagyu, K Inagaki, T Kondo, M Suzuki, N Kanayama, T Terao. Therapeutic efficacy of once-daily oral administration of a Kunitz-type protease inhibitor, bikunin, in a mouse model and in human cancer. Cancer 2004 Feb15:100(4):869-77.

Unlu NZ, Bohn T, Clinton SK, Schwartz SJ. Carotenoid absorption from salad and salsa by humans is enhanced by the addition of avocado or avocado oil. J Nutr. 2005.135(3):431-436.

JQu, LMa, J Zhang, S Jockusch, I Washington, Dietary chlorophyll metabolites catalyze the photoreduction of plasma ubiquinone. Hotochem Photobiol. 2013 Mar-Apr;89(2):310-3.

Bradley A. Maron, M.D. and Joseph Loscalzo, M.D., Ph.D. The Treatment of Hyperhomocysteinemia Annu Rev Med. 2009; 60: 39-54.

Howe GR, Hirohata T, Hislop TG, et al. Dietary factors and risk of breast cancer: combined analysis of 12 case-control studies. J NatL Cancer Inst. 1990;82(7):561-9.

Birt, Diane, Boylston, Terri, Hendrich, Suzanne, Jane et al. Resistant Starch: Promise for Improving Human Health. Adv Nutr. 2013 Nov;4(6)587-601.

Xiao HB, Jun-Fang, Lu XY et al. Protective effects of kaempferol against endothelial damage by an improvement against endothelial damage by an improvement in nitric oxide production and a decrease in asymmetric dimethylarginine level. European Journal of Pharmacology Vol.616, Issue1-3, August2009. Ppg213-222.

Somerset SM, Johannot, L. Dietary flavonoid sources in Australian adults. Nutr. Cancer. 2008;60(4):442-9.

I.A. Lang, T.S. Galloway, A. Scarlett, W.E. Henley, M. Depledge, R.B. Wallace, and D. Melzer. Association of urinary bisphenol a concentration with medical disorders and laboratory abnormalities in adults. Jama, 300-311. 2008.

Papanikolaou Y1, Fulgoni VL 3rd. Bean consumption is associated with greater nutrient intake, reduced systolic blood pressure, lower body weight, and a smaller waist circumference in adults: results fro the National Health and Nutrition Examination Survey. 1999-2002 J Am Coll Nutr. 2008 Oct;27(5):569-76.

Patel, Seema, Gohal, Arun, Recent developments in mushrooms as anti-cancer therapeutics: a review. 3Biotech 2012 Mar;2(1):1-15.

Shu XO, Zheng Y, Cai H, Gu K, Chen Z, Zheng W, Lu W. Soy food intake and breast cancer survival. JAMA 2009 Dec 9;302(22)2437-43.

Paverse JM, Krishna SN, Bergan RC. Genistein inhibits human prostate cancer cell detachment, invasion, and metastasis. Am J Clin Nutr. 2014 Jul;100 Suppl 1:431S-6S.

Juan Wu, Eunyoung Cho,; Willett, Walter C, Intakes of Lutein, Zeaxanthin, and other carotenoids and Age-Related Macular Degeneration During 2 Decades of Prospective Follow-up. JAMA Opthalmol. 2015;133(12):1415-1424.

Li PG, Mu TH, Deng L. Anticancer effects of sweet potato protein on human colorectal cancer cells. World J Gastroenterology. 2013 Jun 7; 19(21)3300-8. Haytowitz D, Ajika J, et al. Composition of Foods Raw, Processed, Prepared. USDA National Nutrient Database for Standard Reference, Release27.

Silke K, Schagen, Vasiliki A., Zampeli, et al. Demato-endocrinology; 2012 Jul1;4(3)298-307.

Scarmo S, Cartmel B, Lin H, Leffell DJ, Welch E, Bhosale P, et al. Significant correlations of dermal total carotenoids and dermal lycopene with their respective plasma levels in healthy adults. Arch Biochem Biophys. 2010; 504:34-9.

Schafer G, Kaschula C., Anticancer Agents Med Chem. 2014 Feb; 14(2):233-240.

United States Department of Agriculture Agricultural Research Service. USAD Food Composition Databases.

Anton D, Bender I, Kaart T, et al. Changes in the Polyphenols Contents and Antioxidant Capacities of Organically and Conventionall Cultivated Tomato (Solanum lycopeersicum L.) Frutis during Ripening. Int J Anal Chem. 2017; 2017: 2367453.

Borguini RG and Torres EAFDS. Tomatoes and Tomato Products as Dietary Sources of Antioxidants. Food Reviews International. Philadelphia: 2009. Vol. 25, Iss. 4;p. 313-325. 2009.

Cheng HM, Koutsidis G, Lodge JK, et al. Tomato and lycopene supplementation and cardiovascular risk factors: A systematic review and meta-analysis. Atherosclerosis. 2017 Feb; 257: 100-108.

Etminan M, Takkouche B, and Caamano-Isorna F. The role oftomato products and lycopene in the preventsion of prostate cancer; a meta –analysis of observational studies. Cancer Epidemiol Biomarkers Prev. 2004 Mar;13(3): 340-5. 2004.

INDEX

Made in the USA
Monee, IL
06 June 2021